Quarterly Essay

Quarterly Essay is published four times a year by Black Inc., an imprint of Schwartz Books Pty Ltd. Publisher: Morry Schwartz.

ISBN 9781760644208 ISSN 1444-884x

Subscriptions – 1 year print & digital (4 issues): $99.99 within Australia incl. GST. Outside Australia $134.99. 2 years print & digital (8 issues): $169.99 within Australia incl. GST. 1 year digital only: $59.99.

Payment may be made by Mastercard or Visa, or by cheque made out to Schwartz Books. Payment includes postage and handling.

To subscribe, fill out and post the subscription card or form inside this issue, or subscribe online:

quarterlyessay.com
subscribe@blackincbooks.com
Phone: 61 3 9486 0288

Correspondence should be addressed to:

The Editor, Quarterly Essay
22–24 Northumberland Street
Collingwood VIC 3066 Australia
Phone: 61 3 9486 0288 / Fax: 61 3 9011 6106
Email: quarterlyessay@blackincbooks.com

Editor: Chris Feik. Management: Elisabeth Young. Publicity: Anna Lensky. Design: Guy Mirabella. Associate Editor: Kirstie Innes-Will. Assistant Editor: Rebecca Bauert. Production Coordinator: Marilyn de Castro. Typesetting: Typography Studio. Figures by Saul Griffith, Josh Ellison and Alan Laver.

Printed in Australia by McPherson's Printing Group. The paper used to produce this book comes from wood grown in sustainable forests.

PREFACE

In a 1951 interview, the French poet and playwright Jean Cocteau was asked, "Suppose flames were consuming your home and time was precious. What one thing would you carry away?"

The famously agile Cocteau replied, "I would carry away the fire."

And so it needs to be with climate change. We need to carry away all of the little fires in our lives, all the blue flames, all the fires from burning fossil fuels, all of which create the global heating that in Australia literally threatens so many of our homes with incineration.

We should carry away the fire. We can do all the things that fire can do with electricity. This is what I mean when I say we must electrify everything. With clean electricity, we can not only cook, heat, drive, refrigerate, make steel, even fly, but we can do these things with no emissions. But we can't do it individually, we can't rely on the market to change fast enough, and we can't wait for governments to take action.

We have to do it ourselves, in our homes and, especially, in our communities.

THE WIRES THAT BIND

Electrification and Community Renewal

Saul Griffith

Have you ever contemplated the miracle that brings you heat, light and convenience? (It will soon bring you transport as well.) The Australian electricity network is the largest machine Australia has ever built. It physically links every single household and every single Australian. Because of this literal connection, we might also see clean electrification as the project that can unite us in a period of dislocation, a nation-building opportunity to define twenty-first-century Australia.

Stand outside your home, look up and you will see coated wires that stretch from your house to the pole nearest your house. Likely there are two layers of wires on the pole, four on the lower level, delivering 240 volts to other homes and neighbours. Above those are three thicker wires on top, your local "string," carrying 11,000 volts around your neighbourhood and back to the substation. For nearly every household, this means that their light bulbs connect to a switchboard that is connected to a meter that is connected to a pair of wires that come from poles on the street that connect them to distribution wires that go down the street and connect to a neighbour. Those distribution wires criss-cross the entire town, physically connecting *every* neighbour.

All those wires come together at a distribution substation. You probably cannot conjure an image of this machine in your mind, but as soon as you see it – often near a railway line or in an industrial corner of your community – you will recognise it. This substation connects your communities with other communities via transmission lines. This interconnecting set of distribution networks all gets tied together in a nationwide gossamer web of copper and aluminium, held safely aloft by tens of millions of distribution poles (many made of wood) and countless transmission towers, typically made of steel. Finishing this picture are the wind, solar and hydroelectricity needed to power the system.

The electricity network connects us more than just physically. It exists because of our common need for energy. To build the physical infrastructure that allows almost every Australian household to access energy with the flick of a switch, we had to build social, organisational, commercial, governmental and political infrastructure. Those systems are even more important to our future, but they are much harder to picture than the network of wires and poles you can see on your block. The illustration below, Figure 1, may help you start to see them. The machines (and wires and poles) are in the middle, but they only exist in the context of the stakeholders and the politics that produce and consume the energy the network brings. To consume energy is to be connected through our governments, our politics and, most of all, our communities.

I want the electricity system to be concrete to you because those wires don't just connect you to every other Australian. They also connect you to the future of our energy system, and to our principal solution in tackling climate change: the electrification of everything. But the role of community and the participation of the household in this revolution must be just as concrete. Real climate action in Australia, and globally, has to happen at the level where citizens interact with their local infrastructure and invest in their homes, businesses and communities, where the literal wires are connected to our heat pumps, electric vehicles, rooftop solar, batteries and appliances. We need an army on the front lines helping every community

Figure 1: The electricity system from appliance to the National Electricity Market

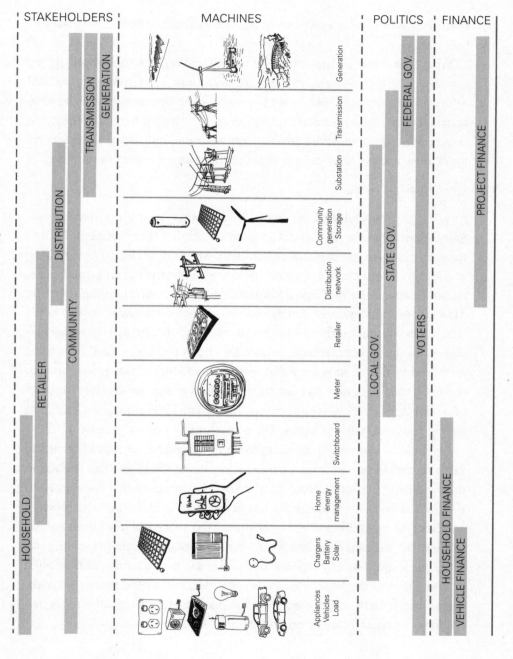

transition. We need a new social contract such that every Australian can join the game.

What is possible is determined by a combination of local council (rules, regulations, physical space), state government (funding, rebates, tax law and infrastructure administered by bodies such as the Department of Education and the Department of Transport) and federal government (emission reduction targets, tax codes, regulatory environment and funding). These are the levers for change, and we must be able to see them clearly if we are to pull them.

My electrification journey

In 2021, the publisher of my book *The Big Switch* arranged a hectic book tour, in two chunks, on the east and south coasts of this continent. I didn't want to fly; since my book was about why we need to electrify everything to address climate change, I wanted to drive an electric car so I could experience firsthand the practical limitations of the national charging network. This was going to mean many hours driving between towns, not to mention hours waiting for the car to charge. I hit upon the idea of spending that time with my mother, Pamela, whom I'd seen less than I would have liked after twenty-five or so years living in the United States. She agreed, and so my book tour became two road trips, one in a rented white Tesla Model 3 obtained through Evee, the other in a Tesla Model 3 Performance loaned to me by Tesla Australia. (Thanks, and sorry for the two flat tyres.)

One reason I was eager for Mum to join me was that we would be seeing vast stretches of the Australian landscape, much of which she had painted or drawn during her long career as an artist. Her image of the Waratah is on the NSW driver's licence, her work is in major collections, and she received an Order of Australia in 2022. Her prints and paintings have been mostly inspired by Australian landscapes, so she is passionate about preserving our land, particularly wetlands. She is one of the few non-scientists to be elected as Councillor of the Royal Society of NSW, Australia's oldest scientific body. For as long as I can remember, Mum has been fighting for good — for equality, for women and for the environment.

This essay in many ways seeks to describe everything I have learned since writing *The Big Switch*, the road trip a literal metaphor for my own journey through the electrification of the Australian economy and new ideas about how we will get the job done. Everywhere we went, we met smart, practical people who showed up already engaged and knowledgeable about this crusade: the need to electrify everything, backed by renewables, to address climate heating and keep our Earth liveable. We had hearty conversations as everyone dug in to figure out how to make clean electrification – solar, batteries, wind power, electric vehicles and appliances – happen in their communities.

It was striking to see how many of these meetings in rural towns were spearheaded by women. (Shortly thereafter, the 2022 "teal wave" crashed over Australian politics, putting even more women into leadership roles.) It became abundantly clear to me that it was primarily women – concerned about the legacy they are leaving their children – who recognised the urgency of change. Women around the country were quietly stepping up to make the changes they saw needed to be made.

What is our shared vision? We can renew our communities, local and national, through electrification and replacing fossil-fuel-burning cars and appliances with ones powered by clean energy. We need to do this to conserve our world, but it also brings other benefits, not least of which are financial, and the best of which is creating wires that bind us to our neighbours and to each other as Australians.

The first stop on our book tour was Albury–Wodonga, on the land of the Wiradjuri, to do a number of events with Helen Haines, the independent member for Indi, who was at the time working on a community battery members' bill for parliament. As I rode on Helen's coat-tails for three days, I witnessed an astonishing example of politics grounded in genuine connection. She was meeting with her community: she was at a solar manufacturer, then an electric truck maker, then a solar farm, then a meeting with the city council of Albury–Wodonga to workshop the decarbonisation of rural households. And she was *listening*.

Everywhere she went, Helen was greeted with smiles. People would interrupt lunch or coffee to offer feedback and suggestions, queries and concerns. Helen blazed through Indi in her signature orange car and orange pants and scarf. She gave me an orange cockatoo pin; she also gave me the rundown on how first Cathy McGowan, and then she, built a new kind of community-oriented politics, a politics of listening and genuinely respecting and representing the community.

To make the transition we must make, we need not just new physical infrastructure but also new ways of leading and particularly of organising at the community level. The leaders I met — nearly all women — are showing us how it's done.

Perhaps the most impressive meeting was our visit to a solar tracker manufacturer. After meeting with the owner of the establishment, Helen made a point of returning to the lunch room to greet and encourage the employees. That spoke volumes. She wants to represent local businesses and advocate for their success, but she equally wants to see the conditions and hear the opinions of the people working hard on the shop floor. She struck me as everyone's representative, not just the representative of the business community or the well-to-do. This shift in political model, with its genuine, big-hearted populism, is also changing the way we can fight climate change.

Protopia

We tend to talk about climate change as a choice between dystopia and utopia, but neither idea is very helpful in getting us to a better future. My friend Kevin Kelly has a concept that rejects both. Kevin is a big thinker (he was an original fixture at the *Whole Earth Catalog* and helped get *Wired* magazine off the ground) and a long-term thinker (he co-founded the Long Now Foundation). He believes that we are constantly seeking a "protopia," or a prototype of utopia, that can serve as a North Star for others. We will always be iterating on protopia, for utopia can't be reached. Protopia is always trying to make the future just a little bit better for our descendants.

I believe Australia can be the first protopia for a zero-emission economy, a North Star to guide the rest of the planet. We have the space, the climate and the resource advantages that make it easier for us. But first, each of our communities needs to be and can be its own protopia of implementation. We can't wait for boffins to give us the answer from on high. It has to happen from the ground up, within and across our communities, as we take action, share our ideas and successes, and (re)build our networks.

In this essay, I want to help you envision a realistic and achievable future. What I won't address here is the international aspect of Australia's climate contribution. Ross Garnaut has written extensively on the opportunity for Australia to be a renewable superpower. I agree with this position, even if I don't agree on the details and the amount of hydrogen we will make and export. I will focus here on our domestic economic opportunity, which I believe to be at least as large, and certainly providing more of a windfall directly to households and everyday Australians.

We need a realistic and achievable vision for the future because the future is coming fast. We have only about one-quarter of one century, twenty-five years, one human generation, to get ourselves out of this climate quandary. If we get this right, if we design the incentives and the policies and the regulations correctly, communities will thrive. Every Australian will benefit economically, socially and even health-wise. So let's hit the road.

While we were driving from Goulburn, on Gundungurra land, stopping to charge at Gundagai on our way to Albury, I told Mum how I had learned a lot about Australians and their relationship with sustainability from my son's Year 6 class project. About a year ago, he informed me (at the last minute, of course) that he had an assignment to design and build a 3D model of a sustainable house that he would take to school. As always, he was creative and bucked the desire to do anything normal. He wanted to dream big and build a floating city of 10,000 people (roughly everyone in our postcode) so that the animals and birds could have the space we currently occupy on the ground and the humans could live in the floating city above, giving nature time and space to recover. I loved the idea and helped him hack some cardboard together with Scotch tape to resemble the thing in his imagination. We calculated that you would need twelve blimps, each four times longer than the Hindenburg, to keep it aloft. Barring practical realities such as storms and lightning, "it should work."

We took this wondrous slapstick model to school the following day. As we approached the building, I could tell from the extra traffic at drop-off and the elaborate models that were being carried in by parents (alongside their kids) that this was a project that had been taken seriously. Every model looked like twenty to forty hours of parent time had been put into it on top of all the kid time. Most architectural offices would have been proud of the detailed dioramas! What was odd, however, was how uniform the solutions were. Virtually every model home looked a lot like the homes that already dot our suburb, only with more solar on the roof, a Tesla in the garage and a chicken coop.

So that was what Australians thought sustainability is: something very similar to what they have today, only a bit nicer and with a chicken coop.

Mum laughed. But this story isn't intended to make fun of the conformity of the Australian suburbs, but rather to acknowledge that although people want change, they want change that doesn't disrupt everything. This shouldn't surprise anyone. Did we really think everyone would become a vegan bicycle commuter overnight? And something crucial follows from this: in real communities, climate action means fixing the buildings and infrastructure that we have. It is largely a retrofit project.

To make the transition to an all-electric economy, we have to carry away the fire and replace all the fossil-fuel machines. While some people resist these changes, the fact is that we've made such changes throughout history. While we drove on our road trip, I got Mum talking about her early years, helping her mother wring sheets by hand, and the excitement of the iceman coming. Her family was one of the first on their block to buy an electric refrigerator, and her grandfather still drove a horse and sulky when she was young. She and my dad bought one of the first countertop dishwashers second-hand almost fifty years ago, and my dad kept their clothes dryer working for nearly thirty years before finally buying a new (electric!) one a few years ago. The transformation to our modern conveniences was huge, and has happened in living memory. We're in the midst of another transition now, to an all-electric future. If you had asked my mother as a little girl what she thought the future would be like, it certainly wouldn't have involved cordless vacuums and electric dishwashers, induction cooktops and electric cars you plug in at charging stations, yet all of those changes happened.

Things change, machines change, and people like changes they can recognise, making things a bit nicer than they were. Because we must make the switch to all-electric machines, I have arrived at thinking about this energy transition as a "machines problem." Machines break. Bearings wear out. Metal rusts. Very few of the machines that were in our lives twenty-five years ago are in our lives today. Most are long gone to the junkyard, recycled for their steel and glass.

What this means is that all the fossil-fuel machines "we can't do without" will fail or fall apart in the next few decades and be replaced by another machine that does the same thing at least as well and probably better. That's the change we can recognise. I find it useful to think through this change-over of machines in more detail so that as individuals, and as a society, we can get on with the job of replacing all the dirty fossil-fuel machines with a whole bunch of clean electric machines powered by renewable energy. Thinking about the machines spreads the responsibility and demonstrates our connectedness. Merely getting industry to decarbonise isn't enough; we need industry to decarbonise while also only making clean electric machines to replace our cars and appliances. Clean electric industry needs to make clean electric things for us to incorporate into our clean electric households.

Every time a dirty fossil machine breaks, we need to replace it with a clean one. As a society, we need to write the rules and regulations to support the clean machines and disincentivise the climate-harming machines. We need to train our workforce to install and maintain these new clean machines.

In that spirit, let's name all the machines, and count them. We need clarity about the job in front of us, a task that implicates all of us. The world we need isn't inconceivably different from the one we are in, but it is one in which we no longer emit carbon dioxide from our human activities. If we think through all the changes that need to happen to ensure people make the right choices replacing all those machines, we will be on our way towards a better, not perfect world − a protopia.

101 million machines...

The energy economy is typically thought of as two sides, supply and demand − where we produce and use our energy, respectively. It's divided into five sectors: Industry, Commercial, Residential, Transport and Electricity. We can count the machines on both sides, and in all sectors.

Let's start at the big end of town, the supply side. There are around 100 coalmines in Australia, with a few dozen loaders to move the coal to power stations and for export. It takes tens of thousands of rail cars travelling on 38,000 kilometres of freight rail lines, pulled by hundreds of locomotives, to get the coal to half a dozen ports and twenty-four coalfired power stations.

We tap 100 million tonnes of gas from around twenty-five offshore rigs and a few thousand terrestrial gasfields. There are 39,000 kilometres of large-scale gas transmission pipelines. Nine LNG terminals compress and cool the gas for export. Seven major storage facilities smooth out the supply seasonally and feed a few thousand natural-gas-fired electricity generators, as well as the 100,000 kilometres of natural gas distribution lines that bring the gas to around 7 million homes and 300,000 businesses, via a gas meter.

The demand side is the smaller machines that we own. Continuing from where we left off, another 1.5 million homes have bottled gas, and all of the gas, metered or bottled, feeds around 6 million gas heaters, 4.8 million gas water heaters, 1.9 million gas freestanding stoves, 2.8 million gas cooktops and 2.3 million gas ovens. Maybe 100,000 of our 1.2 million swimming pools and our hot tubs are heated by gas. There are around 4 million gas barbecues. It is an unpopular truth, but we know that these gas appliances have multiple negative health impacts, including increasing the rates of asthma.

We produce 131 million barrels of oil and import 842 million. Sixty oil tankers bring it to Australia, none of which we own, which represents a serious security risk. The oil travels through 3600 kilometres of pipeline to four refineries that feed thousands of tanker-trucks that deliver to 6500 petrol stations.

Those fuels feed the 20 million vehicles in our garages, 35 per cent of which are passenger vehicles, 45 per cent SUVs and crossovers, 20 per cent utes. There are an additional 500,000 rigid trucks, 105,000 articulated trucks and 97,000 buses. We have 2279 commercial aeroplanes and 9150 in our general aviation fleet. We also love our 1 million boats, and add to that tens of millions of golf carts, ATVs, jetskis, lawnmowers, whipper-snippers and dirt bikes. Industrially, we have half a dozen cement-makers and a dozen smelters and blast furnaces, as well as a few hundred thousand coal and gas boilers and burners.

If we add everything up and round up due to a few tractors we are sure to have overlooked, there are around 1 million supply-side and industrial machines, and around 60 million demand-side residential and commercial machines burning fossil fuels.

To replace all of those with electric machines, we will also need some new infrastructure. That means solar on an additional 5 to 7 million households. Batteries on around 5 million households. Ten or 20 million vehicle chargers, at least one in every garage, some on power poles and in the street, a few at local grocery stores and car parks. Every home will need a Home Energy Management System (HEMS), a dorky acronym for the computer that will manage all the flows of electrons between the things in your life. Some homes will need an upgraded switchboard to carry the extra electricity safely. In round figures, that will mean 30 to 40 million new machines in supporting roles for our electric future. Add them up and there are 101 million machines between us and a zero-emission fleet of Australian homes and small businesses.

What is hard to decarbonise?

Aviation, freight transport, industry and agriculture are described by some people as the "hard-to-decarbonise" sectors. But these machines are few. A few dozen coal loaders, a few hundred ships, a few thousand planes, a couple of blast furnaces, a few smelters, dozens of locomotives. We are told these sectors are hard to decarbonise because there isn't a solution yet, or because it is expensive, or threatens business. But in every case the technology is on the way. I sometimes think the "hard-to-decarbonise" sectors are merely entrenched businesses that have lobby groups complaining loudly, hoping for a subsidy before they do the right thing. These industries need less subsidy than they are lining up for, and we need to consider that in fact the truly hard-to-decarbonise sector is the 101 million machines, each requiring a purchasing decision, a financing or banking moment, a supply chain and a willing workforce.

The good news is that we will replace these 101 million machines with ones that are much better. We now have EVs in every shape and size for every type of family and for every need. We have electric induction cooktops that heat faster, are easier to clean, enable more control, result in a cooler kitchen and don't emit toxic gases inside your home. We have electric heat pump water heaters that use one-third of the energy of natural gas water heaters. We have reverse cycle air conditioners and heat pumps that can replace your oil boiler or your gas furnace, using one-third of the energy.

Even those who resist these changes – witness the fetishism of gas stoves by cooks who have never tried induction models – will come to appreciate them for their efficiency and clean technology (no changing the oil in the car). While we were driving, my mother recalled the man who would drive an ice truck to her house when she was a very little girl. She described the smell of the hemp sacks that kept the ice from melting and the leather straps and bands and the ice picks that were his tools of trade. She also remembers when most of the groceries were delivered to the houses on the street because few women drove and it was impractical to go daily to the store: everything from fresh bread to milk, even butchered rabbits shot locally during the rabbit plague. That was in Rockdale, only ten or so kilometres from Sydney's CBD. When she was about seven, she remembers moving into a house with an electric refrigerator. The refrigerator made everything easier. The refrigerator, it should be remembered, was the first mass adoption of the very, very useful and multi-talented heat pump.

My mother told a further hilarious story about the "poo man," who used to come and take away the contents of the septic tank, and the day he dropped the contents on the driveway and she saw her poo floating down the street on a river of household pee. Shortly after, they got a flushing toilet installed in the house, in the late 1940s or early 1950s. Apparently, barbecues were being popularised at the same time, and she remembers the joke of the day was about the fellow who, when asked how his life was going, replied, "Terrific! I now shit inside and eat outside!"

The point is that the future happens, and is happening all the time, and what was common one generation can be gone the next. Cultures last a long time, but machines are transient. We can't let our attachment to them keep us from envisioning a different future.

The phenomenon of consumer uptake of things is understood as an adoption curve, sometimes referred to as an experience rate. Examples of adoption curves are shown in Figure 2. Consumer electronic devices such as mobile phones and colour TVs only took about twenty years to be adopted by practically all households. Things that require infrastructure, such as landline telephones, took longer because the deployment was slowed down by the necessity of stringing all the lines. Even something as practical as the flushing toilet took longer because it required modifications to our housing stock.

The second chart in Figure 2 illustrates the theoretical shapes and speed of adoption curves under different policy and regulatory circumstances. In theory, the government could mandate that tomorrow it will come and replace all gas stoves with electric ones. This is the "magic wand" scenario. We'd have zero-emission cooking nationally, overnight. But this isn't practical: people would rebel, the supply chain would break and the workforce isn't prepared to do it. It is already hard enough to find a tradie to electrify the kitchen.

The best you might be able to do in practice is replace it when it fails. Everything gets replaced eventually except for the few things that become museum pieces. A government could institute a 'no new gas stove/petrol vehicle/gas heater' policy after a certain year, say 2025. After 2025, when you went to Harvey Norman or asked a tradie to do the kitchen renovation, the only options available would be clean, zero-emission, electric ones. This would result in the 100 per cent at end-of-life replacement curve. If all the stoves last fifteen years, it would take fifteen years after that end date of 2025 to get to an almost completely zero-emission fleet of Australian stoves/cars/heaters.

In 2017, the Norwegian government instituted a no-new-fossil-fuel-vehicles-after-2025 policy. This gave people and the industry a target and enough time for infrastructure to be planned and workforce development to be done. It results in an adoption curve that looks more like the "production ramp-up, then 100 per cent replacement" curve in the second graph of the figure. Subsidies, tax incentives and rebates are other policy mechanisms that can shift the shapes of these curves.

Adoption curves describe not just consumer technologies but things like coal-fired power generation. Because coal-fired electricity generation is pretty much the worst possible thing to do climate-wise, and responsible

Figure 2: Adoption curves for various technologies and for decarbonisation solutions

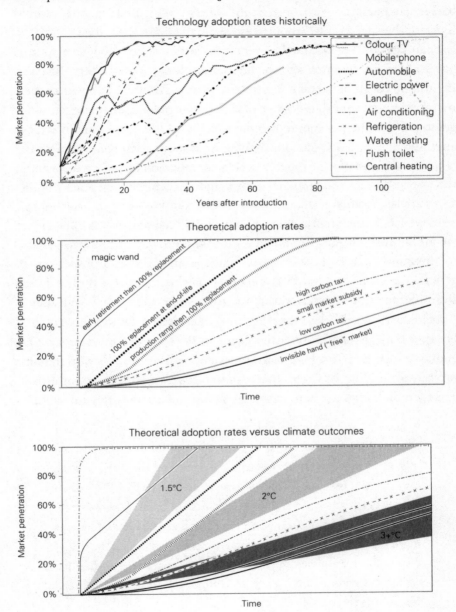

for the largest portion of emissions, scientists, activists and now policy-makers are pursuing "early retirement" of coal. We can see how this would increase the speed of decarbonisation significantly in the curves.

I can hear the free-market conservatives shriek at the thought of all this government interference, and the libertarians at the loss of liberty involved in limiting consumer choice, but the third part of Figure 2 tells you a sobering story. If we want to hit better than 2°C as a global climate target, we've got to go with 100 per cent replacement at end-of-life. If we want to achieve anything like the 1.5°C outcome, which is what our coral reefs, glaciers and children demand of us, we really need a combination of early retirement of the heaviest emitters, combined with mandated replacement at end-of-life. Our cars last twenty years; our appliances about the same. If, starting this year, we had perfect replacement at end-of-life, that means it is 2043 before we are mostly zero-emission, and even so there will be some stragglers.

Mum and I made a lot of stops on our trip, and I did a lot of speaking to general, specialist and political audiences on this topic. It was clear to me from the questions I received that my message wasn't terribly well understood. People heard "Electrify Everything," but then went to a place of guilt because they thought it required them to do everything yesterday. One audience member, Tim Hodgson, contacted me later. He was working on a project called "My Net Zero," based around his own family's commitment, and then planning, to get to zero emissions. In approximately his words:

> A year ago, my family pledged net-zero 2025. We made a plan. Get solar in 2022, financed to reduce the up-front burden. Use the savings from that exercise to electrify the stove and the water heating over the next two years. Then we plan to get a battery in 2024, when the prices have dropped and the economics are better. Finally we will get an electric car in 2025, when the choices are higher and there is more supply and more second-hand options. They are all the things responsible for emissions that we have direct control over. After that we'll focus on our banking and on composting and eating well and consuming responsibly.

Tim later admitted to me that he was waiting for the VW electric Kombi to be available in Australia before he electrified the car. I fetishise Kombis old and new, so I wasn't going to criticise! In fact, I think his is the perfect summary for how we get the job done on time. The Kombi they wanted came as the reward at the end of the already-rewarding process of decarbonising their home.

Every Australian household needs a plan, and the plan needs to replace the things in their life that emit CO_2. It doesn't have to be done immediately, but at the natural rate at which household things break or get replaced. I have summarised this concept in Figure 3 because I think it is unbelievably important, although simple, and it gives us a framework to think about Project Decarbonise Australia – or Rewiring Australia.

Every household will go on a journey of electrification over the next two decades; we can make that project easier, and cheaper, as a nation, or we can make it harder and more expensive. We can optimise the building codes, train the workforce, provide regulatory certainty and phase-out dates that provide market certainty. We can reform the tax code around these purchases, and build these ideas into the way we design social housing and low-income assistance. We could invent schemes that use mechanisms such as those behind the Higher Education Contribution Scheme (HECS) to help everyone come along for the ride. We can make this project go faster, and get a better climate outcome, or we can let it go slower and get a worse one.

It is worth thinking about the small number of decisions that are represented in these charts – when they happen, how they happen and who participates. Very often these upgrades will be lined up with a home purchase or a major renovation. There will be tradespeople involved for all of them, even the car, given that it'll come with a vehicle charger to be installed somewhere. The best possible time to do many of these things is when the home is built, not later as a retrofit, though – to be clear-eyed about the task – we probably will only build a million or so homes over this time, so the challenge is very much a retrofit one, as we've got 10 million households to get to zero. I'm in favour of designing policies similar

Figure 3: (a) The small number of purchasing decisions that get a household's energy "infrastructure" to zero emissions (b) Every household will take a different journey in the sequence of these purchases, but collectively this is the path to zero emissions for the community

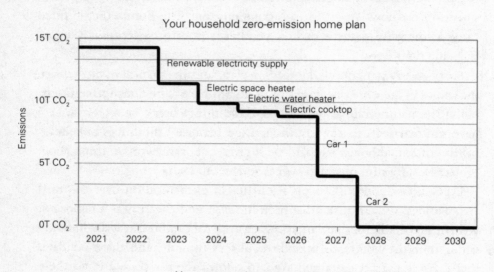

Your household zero-emission home plan

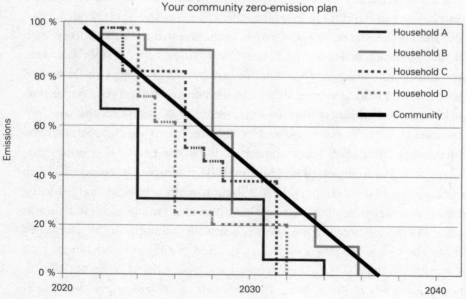

Your community zero-emission plan

to those of the US *Inflation Reduction Act*, which target these decision points and provide incentives at the moments of purchase, whether they be tax incentives, rebates or subsidies.

Before you get worried that this transition sounds big and hard – and it is – remember that we have twenty years to get those machines installed. If we just go with the status quo, we will be buying and installing 100 million machines over the next twenty years anyway. (For example, we buy cars at the rate of one million per year, or at least we did before COVID.) So you don't need to run out and mortgage your house or take out a loan to buy all these electric things in 2023, but rather plan out the pathway for your household to become all-electric by 2025/30/35 or 2040.

When your old Camry or Volvo kicks the bucket, get an electric vehicle. That might be 2024, but it could be 2030. When the water heater goes out, make sure to replace it with a heat pump electric (or even just a resistance electric if it can do demand response). The next time you do a kitchen renovation, select an induction cooktop and electric oven. Replace the gas heaters with reverse-cycle air conditioning and not only decarbonise your winter heat but add cooling for the summer.

We don't have to switch out all our machines tomorrow. We don't need to feel guilty about not having ticked off the full kit yet. Because the electrification industry and supply chain isn't at full scale yet, every time one of these updated electric machines gets purchased and installed, the products get cheaper, the supply chain matures and the machines get better.

When I am my mother's age, I will tell stories to my grandchildren about quaint old things called carburettors and how genuinely infuriating they were, and about replacing LPG tanks when the barbecue sputtered out. I'm sure they will be flabbergasted at the idea that we once had open fires in the kitchen. I'll recount tales of oil fires from making hot chips at home and they'll look at me cross-eyed at the stupidity of it all.

ELECTRIFICATION IS ANTI-INFLATIONARY

At every stop along our journey, my mother and I met with people in town halls and community centres who had concerns about climate change and questions about how to afford the switch to electrification. We will need support to buy the new machines, as you will see, but what is clear is that if we succeed in electrifying Australia, it will keep money in our communities that otherwise would leave in the form of payments at the petrol pump to faraway corporations. The benefits of electrification are lasting.

We can look at the history of the always-increasing total cost of energy for Australian households run on fossil fuels from 1990 to 2020. I present this graph in Figure 4. Further, we can project forward the cost of energy for an Australian household with all-electric appliances, heat and vehicles, powered by renewables. This chart tells an extraordinary story of possibility, especially coming in an inflationary cost-of-living crisis such as Australians are experiencing in 2023. The black line tracing upwards from 1990 is the total cost of energy for an average Australian household. This is the total sum of money spent on petrol, diesel, LPG, electricity and natural gas in the course of a year. It travels upwards and to the right, increasing year on year at roughly the rate of inflation. This is what I call "fossil-flation."

This shouldn't be terribly surprising, since inflation is calculated by the "consumer price index," comprising a basket of goods that includes our (fossil) fuels. The marginal cost of extracting fossil fuels is increasing over time, as the resources become scarcer and of lower concentration and quality. The cost of externalities is increasingly being priced in, producing a more realistic higher figure. From around $2000 a year in 1990, it is now up at $5000 to $6000 a year. Due to the extraordinary inflation and supply chain disruptions of 2022, caused by, among other things, the war in Ukraine and COVID-19, the cost is tipping $7000 a year in 2022/23. Based on the trend of the last thirty years, by 2050 homes are forecast to be paying over $9500 a year in energy bills (dotted line).

Figure 4: History of total cost of energy per average Australian household and forecast if total household is electrified

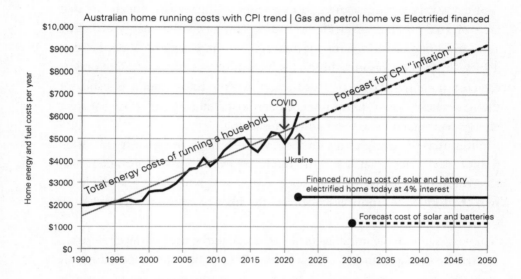

Source: ABS CPI June 2022, AEMC Price Trends 2020, Gas Price Trends Review 2017 Oakley Greenwood, Australian Petroleum Institute, Rewiring Australia. Based on running costs of average gas home energy use. Average home uses petrol, gas and grid electricity. Future prices based on linear trend from historic CPI. Electrified home costs include financed cost of solar and battery at 4 per cent over their warrantied lifetime of twenty-five years and ten years, respectively, excludes cost of appliances and vehicles in both. Battery storage used is 50 per cent of total home energy use.

That is the bad news side of the chart. The good news side is the one that looks forward. This is the thick black line set at around $2000 per year. This is what the cost of energy would be for a fully electrified Australian household were someone to wave a magic wand and replace all the gas appliances with state-of-the-art electric appliances, and the 1.8 petrol or diesel vehicles in the "average" Australian driveway with 1.8 electric vehicles. It assumes the household is fully utilising its rooftop solar (finance for this capacity is included in the estimate) and mixing that 50 per cent of electricity with the average price of zero-emission electricity purchased retail from the grid.

Clean electrification is the transformation of our energy economy away from one based on (relatively) low-cost machines that require expensive future fossil-fuel purchasing commitments to higher-cost machines that are powered by cheaper clean electricity. This turns the energy economy away from one of fuels to one of finance, and the beauty of finance is that it locks in the cost of something. It is literally anti-inflationary. Not only is the cost of energy about one-third going into the future, but it is stable for the next twenty years! Once financed and installed on your roof, that solar energy requires just the fixed cost of financing.

Given that the likely result for fossil fuels through this energy transition is increased price volatility, what might be even more important is that electrification of households makes energy costs predictable and stable far into the future. No more price shocks the likes of which we have seen in the past few years.

If we generalise the numbers provided above to the national level, Australians will be saving up to $40 billion a year. This can be understood intuitively because we won't need to spend $40 billion on foreign oil as we currently do. There will also be savings from solar and wind power replacing our gas and coal, but the biggest saving is from this swap of cheap solar power running electric vehicles for petroleum products. This is captured in Figure 5.

What is demonstrated in this graph is an estimate of the cost of investing in Australian households *as though they were infrastructure*, and what the net benefit to the economy would be as we saw those investments result in greatly reduced energy expenditure. The underlying model involves subsidy of electrification in the early days as we get the market to scale, the workforce in place, and squirt the technological glue that will hold the whole system together. It is as though every time someone's old car croaks it, we underwrite the difference between the cost of the fossil-fuel vehicle that would have replaced it and the cost of an equivalent electric car. Same for natural gas appliances. As the market reaches scale, the cost of EVs falls, the cost of batteries falls and the soft costs of installing and wiring everything together falls. By about 2025, the economics of all the pieces of the solution

Figure 5: Nationwide economic impact of total household electrification

Cumulative spending and savings with subsidised household electrification program

Gradual ramp in household electrification to 100% electrified in 2030

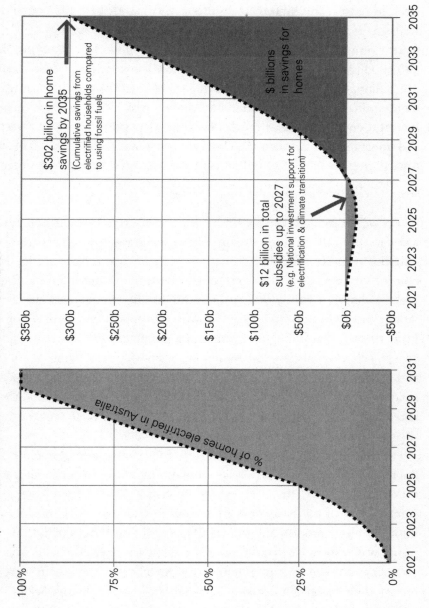

$302 billion in home savings by 2035

(Cumulative savings from electrified households compared to using fossil fuels)

$ billions in savings for homes

$12 billion in total subsidies up to 2027

(e.g. National investment support for electrification & climate transition)

% of homes electrified in Australia

Source: Castles and Cars technical study 2021, Rewiring Australia.

work in most places, and the subsidies can fall so that by 2027 or so none at all are required and we collectively start realising the savings.

Year on year the savings increase, and by 2030 we will be saving about $40 billion a year. The total investment before we get to profitability is about $12 billion, and by 2030 we are saving more than three times that investment annually. It is only a computer model, which can be imperfect, but even if it costs us twice as much ($24 billion) to get to parity and we only end up saving half as much ($20 billion a year), it still looks like an extraordinary investment, as $24 billion now saves us $200 billion next decade.

The largest wealth transfer in human history

As we were driving between Albury and Melbourne, I would stop periodically to take calls from media or policy organisations to discuss the latest setbacks in the continuing negotiations with off-again, on-again Joe Manchin of Virginia, a US Democrat senator with significant interests in fossil fuels, including a family coal business. My mother would overhear conversations about political strategy and how to get support for this detail or that. I had learned that policy isn't written by politicians but rather by interest groups and lobbyists, so, to counter the heavyweight lobbying of coal, gas and oil, the organisation I founded in 2019, Rewiring America, had leaned in and forged alliances with climate and consumer groups around the US and maintained weekly video conferences with energy policy-makers in the White House and with various coalitions.

Electrification can have a profound effect in keeping wealth in our households and communities. While we were driving, I told Mum about my trip to Washington, DC, in 2021, where Rewiring America was hosting the launch party of the bicameral Electrification Caucus, the US mayors' coalition for electrification and the US CEOs' coalition for electrification. The mood was festive, electrification as a catalyst for bold climate action was gathering momentum, and the founding members of the caucus were laying out their visions for decarbonising America. Representative Sean Casten of Illinois said it better than anyone:

> This will be the largest transfer of wealth in human history, from the
> traditional suppliers of energy to the traditional consumers of energy.

What he was describing are the new winners in the global energy transition. The losers will be the centralised (fossil-,fuel) energy companies selling coal, gas and oil. The winners will be in the localised, decentralised energy economy, where many more people own the technologies for generating and storing energy, much of it produced locally in their communities. With solar on roofs, churches, surf clubs, schools and parking lots that is charging our cars and powering our homes, income will be made in the community. Money that would previously have left town to pay for petrol/diesel/gas could now stay, to circulate among the cafes, craftspeople, artisans and tradespeople. A few local employees running a petrol station owned by far-off corporations will make way for local solar installers and tradies putting in induction cooktops and heat pumps. Average people will have more money to spend at their local pub, bookstore or greengrocer.

Later at the same event, my colleague and co-founder of Rewiring America Alex Laskey went on to say:

> In an increasingly divided world, with cultural and political divisions
> amplifying, electrifying represents very concretely the thing that can
> not only metaphorically but literally connect our communities and
> reconnect ourselves. Every home linked by wires to the same grid,
> generating and sharing energy with our neighbours and supporting
> each other through the energy transition.

The machine's-eye view of the energy system helped shape the *Inflation Reduction Act*, with close to half of its investment coming as direct demand-side incentives to households and small businesses to cleanly electrify. It took another six months for President Joe Biden's signature climate legislation to pass through Congress, and thousands of people were involved in its creation. Upon passage it would represent the largest ever commitment to addressing climate change and meeting the targets that will keep us below 2°C of warming.

Of course my mum did not entirely dominate the conversation as we drove around the country. At seventy-nine, she has some hearing loss, and I do too: I did too much windsurfing in cold water and developed classic Australian surfer's ear. One marvellous thing about a road trip in a largely silent electric car is that you can actually hear each other talk.

My side of the conversation was mostly about what I'd been up to in the United States while I was away, and my continuing work there after returning to Australia. My largest remaining commitment to the US is the work I am helping to steer at Rewiring America. After the election of Joe Biden as president, we saw a gap in policy-making on climate around the demand side of the energy system, so we hired policy wonks, former administration officials and some technical and economic analysts and rolled up our sleeves to help write legislation. The book I had completed with MIT Press, *Electrify*, was something of a policy template we used to guide our thinking, drawing on an extremely deep analysis of the US energy system I performed with colleagues at the Department of Energy.

The 2022 US climate bill, the *Inflation Reduction Act* (IRA), has been summarised as carrots, carrots and more carrots. In combination with the *Defense Production Act* (DPA) and the *Infrastructure Investment and Jobs Act* (IIJA), it embodies the Biden administration's effort to eliminate carbon emissions from the American economy. Put simply, the IRA sets out to "electrify everything" through incentives that transform the market for clean energy. It is broadly popular precisely because it is incentive-based, not punitive as a carbon tax might have been, and focuses on the household and voter, as opposed to being strictly an industrial policy or set of regulations. This was by necessity rather than inclination: since the Democrats didn't have a sixty-seat, filibuster-proof majority in the Senate, they could not bring the bill through as legislation, but rather had to implement climate policy as a spending bill. This all-carrot approach is good, but it isn't as good as having regulatory certainty, which would give the market certainty, which would make businesses plan very concretely for a zero-emission future. An example from

Europe is the regulatory certainty of Norway banning new fossil-fuel vehicles after 2025.

Figure 6 provides a detailed breakdown of IRA spending using data from the Congressional Budget Office. The CBO's estimate might well be very low, as the spending is not capped. If the IRA is implemented well, and American households take full advantage, it could release closer to US$900 billion in demand-side electrification incentives. That is only the beginning of the massive transfer of wealth we've been talking about. The real wealth accumulation begins not with the subsidies of machines, but in communities once they have electrified and continue to save money instead of spending it on fossil fuels.

About half of the IRA electrification money is for the supply of clean electricity (US$150 billion), either as production credits (US$50 billion) or infrastructure investment credits (US$50 billion). This is important. For our energy system to reach zero emissions, eventually we will require three times the electricity that is delivered today.

A further $40 billion is dedicated to the manufacturing of both supply-side and demand-side electrification machines, whether vehicles, batteries, heat pumps, solar, wind or even electric kitchen appliances.

Key to the IRA was placing the demand side — where Americans use energy in their homes, vehicles and small businesses — on an equal footing with the production of zero-emission electricity. The demand-side incentives in the IRA (US$140 billion) include low-cost financing, direct electric vehicle rebates and incentives, and several incentives to electrify appliances and buildings. The intent of these investments is to permanently transform the marketplace for these machines in the United States, such that eventually the only available product will be a zero-emission option. If you want a new stove, it will be an induction stove; if you want a new car, it will be electric. Fossil-fuelled cars will become as obsolete as my great-grandfather's horse and sulky.

The IRA directly engages with American households. Each will have access to an average of $14,000 in up-front discounts to switch to electric appliances in their home. Some low-income households will qualify for having all of the cost of electrifying appliances covered; moderate-income homes, half. In addition to up-front discounts, the IRA also includes tax credits for electrification and efficiency upgrades. Up-front discounts on the purchase of EVs of up to $7500 for new cars and $4000 for used cars can be accessed from 2024, extending existing incentives. The IRA provides 30 per cent off the cost of rooftop solar, home batteries and geothermal systems. This is a big incentive in the US, where the installation cost is significantly higher than in Australia.

This US investment in electrification not only benefits households but also creates jobs. By one estimate, if households take full advantage of the IRA, it will generate 1.4 million direct jobs in electrification and 5 million new jobs overall. However, it is worth noting that the IRA is short on incentives to electrify industry. There is very little new research funding for the sectors where we still need to take zero-emission solutions beyond lab scale: heavy industry, high-temperature industrial heat, cement, steel, metals, mining and agriculture. When I encourage Australia to be ambitious, it's because this is a sector that is wide open for us to become global leaders. No one else is yet tackling this problem at the level required.

The IRA poses a threat if Australia isn't at least as ambitious. The United States is favouring domestic manufacturing to keep the production and assembly of solar, batteries, electric vehicles, heat pumps and even electric appliances within the US. The IRA is intended to permanently alter US and global supply chains and the workforce towards electric appliances, electric vehicles and clean and renewable electricity. Unless Australia matches its intensity and ambition, it could find itself the dumping ground of last century's technologies as corporations focus their supply chains towards the United States.

The Australian government would be well advised to build its own version of the *Inflation Reduction Act*, and in reality we can be more ambitious. Unlike in the US, where a divided Congress struggles to agree on much of anything other than Daylight Savings Time, Australia can legislate rather than just direct spending. We could legislate improved building codes, zero-emission vehicle standards and sunset dates for fossil-fuel machines.

Australia has many natural advantages that can make it a leader in the decarbonisation economy. It leads the world in rooftop solar, household batteries and the digital integration of these assets. Our mild climate and relatively high prices for petrol, diesel and natural gas mean that the economics of electrification are more attractive here than in the United States. With a large commitment to electrification, Australia can reap the economic savings sooner, pass the savings onto families and achieve the near-term emissions reductions required to meet and exceed our emissions targets.

In this more ambitious legislation, Australia should provide accessible and affordable finance and incentives to support households to electrify. We should also invest in electrifying public and social housing to ensure an equitable transition. We should demonstrate intensive electrification through community pilots, build the skilled workforce for installation and maintenance of this 21st-century technology, and optimise local, state and federal codes and regulations. The government should support Australia's role in the global supply chain of modern electric appliances, electric vehicles and renewable sources of electricity. Our primary industry and manufacturing sectors have critical roles to play, particularly in the provision of the key metals and minerals of this global energy transition – steel, aluminium, copper, lithium, silicon, nickel, tin, cobalt and other rare-earth elements.

To be clear, as ambitious and precedent-setting as it was, the IRA will not reduce emissions by the more than 50 per cent by 2030 that is required for a chance at 1.5°C. Jesse Jenkins of Princeton University perhaps optimistically suggested it can get 42 per cent and set us on a path for around 2 to 2.5°C if every country follows suit. The legislation was ambitious, but we need the world to continue to ratchet up ambition. Ideally, Australia would be more ambitious than the United States and create a bold precedent for Europe, Asia and the US. We need ambition to beget more ambition with every legislative opportunity. It is in our economic and environmental interest to lead, not follow.

Shortly after this essay will be published, Australia will announce some electrification policies in the 2023 Budget. If we were to spend pro-rata what the United States did in its IRA, we'd be legislating to invest $40–50 billion over ten years, half in incentives directly to households and small businesses, and the other half to the industrial and supply side. It's time for an Australian *Inflation Reduction Act*. I hope it has a better name – the *Electrifying Communities Act*? It should address the cost of living and the climate in a permanent way by installing low-cost clean energy in every household and community – a set of measures that transform the energy marketplace. This means not only incentives, but also reforming tax law, a huge push on job and skills training for an all-electric workforce, and appropriate infrastructure investments, such as transmission, vehicle charging and storage. Best of all would be government-backed loan guarantees or similar mechanisms that help every Australian take the electrification journey and reap the benefits.

NEO-CAPITALIST COMMUNITARIANISM

As much as it was hobbled by US politics, the *Inflation Reduction Act* is feeling its way towards a new politics. Joe Biden was comparatively quiet about it, as befits the contemporary keep-your-head-down divisions in US politics. I had hoped for more Rooseveltian leadership on the subject:

> True leadership calls for the setting forth of the objectives and the rallying of public opinion in support of these objectives.
>
> Do not confuse objectives with methods. When the nation becomes substantially united in favor of planning the broad objectives of civilization, then true leadership must unite thought behind definite methods.
>
> The country needs and, unless I mistake its temper, the country demands bold, persistent experimentation. It is common sense to take a method and try it: If it fails, admit it frankly and try another. But above all, try something.

To make the transition to electrification, we are going to have to engage in a new kind of politics, focused on communities. We haven't yet fully invented that politics. It will require bold, persistent experimentation.

In his 2022 book *The Rise and Fall of the Neoliberal Order*, Gary Gerstle defines what he calls a "political order" as a set of ideas that become so pervasive they transcend the differences between political parties. He uses two canonical examples from the United States. Franklin D. Roosevelt's New Deal, once fiercely contested by the Republicans, was embraced and continued by the Republican president Dwight Eisenhower; he could not fight it. The triumph of the next political order came decades later, when Democrat Bill Clinton embraced the politics of deregulation and free trade championed by Ronald Reagan, which came to be known as neoliberalism.

In Australia, we experienced neoliberalism under a different brand name: economic rationalism. As laid out in Michael Pusey's 1992 book *Economic Rationalism in Canberra: A Nation-building State Changes Its Mind*, Australia had its own high-water mark of government intervention with the Whitlam government and then the same kind of backlash when economic rationalism – our Down Under variant of the same neoliberal playbook – took over Canberra.

Returning to Gerstle's framing of US history, you see the role of crisis in triggering a new political order. The New Deal arose out of the crisis of the Great Depression. Old policies had failed utterly. Most of the new policies that were tried had also failed, but a spirit of ruthless experimentation, led in particular by Roosevelt's Secretary of Labor, Frances Perkins, eventually led to the creation of the minimum wage, unemployment insurance, social security and other features of the modern welfare state.

But the change also required an intellectual framework. Economist John Maynard Keynes provided that framework, arguing that aggregate demand was the problem, not supply, that the market would not automatically correct itself, and that large-scale government spending was required.

This "big government" New Deal order was exported to Europe after the war via the Marshall Plan, and eventually embraced by both parties in the United States. As President Eisenhower put it in a letter to one of his critics, "Should any political party attempt to abolish social security and unemployment insurance and eliminate labor laws and farm programs you would not hear of that party again in our political history."

A change in political order typically comes over time in response to the failure of the old order to deliver its promised benefits. The New Deal order hit its limits in the 1970s as a result of high inflation. This was in part triggered by the power of organised labour to gain higher wages, leading to a so-called wage-price spiral, with the formation of OPEC and the surging price of oil delivering the final crushing blow.

The ideas of Friedrich Hayek, Ludwig von Mises, Milton Friedman and other members of the Mont Pelerin Society provided the intellectual framework for neoliberalism (and economic rationalism). They had been developing an alternative to Keynesianism for decades, based on a return to low taxes and unfettered markets, including a rollback of the power of organised labour. Their emphasis was on harnessing the power of the supply side of the market to create rising prosperity.

As Milton Friedman put it, "Only a crisis – actual or perceived – produces real change. When that crisis occurs, the actions that are taken depend on the ideas that are lying around. That, I believe, is our basic function: to develop alternatives to existing policies, to keep them alive and available until the politically impossible becomes the politically inevitable."

Another aspect of a change in political order is that at least in some proportion it is based on fear. Gerstle describes how important answering the economic threat posed by communism was to making the high taxes, social support systems and pro-labour conditions of the New Deal politically necessary, and how the fall of the Soviet Union relieved the competitive pressure and paved the way to the neoliberal order, along with its dramatic rise in inequality.

Gerstle argues that the neoliberal political order is collapsing, and has been since the 2008 financial crisis, but he has little to say about what comes next. A few have remarked that climate catastrophe is both the final crisis that will bring an end to neoliberalism and the heart of the opportunity for an entire new political order. There will come a time when no one in any political party will be able to deny the crisis or the economic benefits of transcending it.

The case can be made that Joe Biden is fumbling towards a new New Deal (the failed predecessor to the current legislation was even referred to as "the Green New Deal"). Meanwhile, there are only too many conservatives globally who would be delighted for a return to the 1990s world order. What we should all be hoping for is a new, different way that doesn't make a false choice between support for the supply side or the demand side of the economy. If we structure the program correctly, decarbonisation through electrification provides benefits to both supply and demand sides, to businesses and to consumers. Call me a radical centrist. My co-founder of Rewiring America, Alex Laskey, put it very wisely as we planned how to build the organisation: "Lasting political change comes from forming the coalition of the winners."

There are aspects of both the labour union and social infrastructure world order and the globalist capitalist world order that are worth keeping, but neither view is capable by itself of dealing with climate change and escalating inequality. What might the answer be?

In 2022, I was invited to a wonderful conference in New Zealand called Toru, held in Glenorchy. It was a conference of big issues and bigger ideas, at which I spoke about the *Inflation Reduction Act*, energy, climate and electrification. The most extraordinary aspect was the attendees. The minister for climate change was there from the NZ Green Party. The leader of the opposition party was in the room. Representatives from the prime minister's office were there. All of them sat in the same room listening to the same talks.

At question time and in subsequent conversations they all took as given that climate change is real and that solutions are needed quickly, and they reached agreement that electrification is key to the solutions. Apart from dealing with methane emissions from their sheep, they all recognised that curbing household emissions, including vehicles, was the biggest opportunity to solve long-standing inequities around energy affordability, emissions and access.

It was the beginning of a new political order, one in which all points on the political spectrum were agreeing on a core idea: renewable electrification as a means of restructuring the energy system. There wasn't perfect agreement on the details by any means, but all sides were thinking through the implications in line with their existing ideologies, as opposed to opposing the core idea on ideological grounds.

On a trip to Canada only a week or so earlier, I had a much more unsettling experience talking about the same ideas and material. I was at a conference hosted by the Center for American Progress, a US Democratic think-tank run by political consultant John Podesta in partnership with the Canadian government. Also in attendance was Mark Carney, former head of the Bank of England, and a smattering of international democratic leaders.

After I gave a talk similar to the one I was soon to give in New Zealand, the conversation about the future and climate took a darker turn, reflective of the mood I felt on the streets of Toronto, where the conference was held, and as I am told is the mood in England. These very serious political strategists and economists confided that unless climate solutions bring with them a new social contract, a new "American Dream," or promise of making things, life and everyday experience "better," "easier" and more "equitable," they were struggling to believe that democracies as we know them would survive.

This dark view mirrored my own experience living in America. I arrived in 1998, when Silicon Valley and this new thing called the internet were both flourishing. Then came the dot-com crash of late '99 and 2000, followed by the Gore–Bush election of 2000, which had to be decided by the Supreme Court. That very partisan outcome was the moment I could feel a step change. September 11 changed everything even more, and ushered in two long and unsuccessful wars. Living on the ground in the United States during the past twenty years was like watching something great slowly unravel. The social contract had been breached. Things were getting worse for most people, and the poorest Americans were suffering the most.

The neoliberal order is failing to deliver. I have felt the discontent on four continents. I might not state it as darkly as my hosts in Toronto, but I do think that if we are to address climate change we need at least a reasonably stable political system, we need democracy to work, and we need a vision for the future that engages real people, everyday people, not just the international glitterati. What excites me about Australia, and perhaps has contributed to my return to live here, is that I think we have one of the best shots at creating that future here, first, in Australia. If we do so, we can be a (solar-powered!) beacon for other economies. I don't know the name of this new political order, but I hope to help you see the fuzzy outlines of possibility that I see.

I've called this part of the essay "Neo-capitalist Communitarianism" for a reason. I don't think we can kill or reform capitalism in time to save the planet, and we need capitalist signals, market structures, investment mechanisms and entrepreneurship to give us solutions and to finance them. But

I also believe that we need a stronger focus on communities and a reorganisation of the capitalist economy around communities, if for no other reason than that they can be nimble, they can be laboratories, and (as I hope) they can evolve faster to usher in a better world order. The challenges of climate change need a politics of the collective more than a politics of the individual. We only succeed together; we are inextricably linked by the carbon levels in our atmosphere. No matter how wealthy you are, climate disruption will find you, as the poor already know.

The electricity network is both our social and technological way to address these elevated carbon levels. It is a human-made solution to a human-made problem, but the answer only works at a collective level. They are the wires that bind.

So how does this play out in the communities I visited on my road trip? With apologies to economists, I'm going to outline the potential for community economic renewal, and then make the economic case to change the way we think about energy infrastructure.

Community economic renewal

The case for the economically corrosive effect of centralised retailers on communities is well laid out in the books *Big-Box Swindle* by Stacy Mitchell and *The Wal-Mart Effect* by Charles Fishman. In essence, a large-market-funded company comes to a community, and can afford to lose money on its grocery/retail/hardware business until the local business that it replaces fails, giving it a local monopoly. This is why there are fewer butchers, independent grocers and so on in the United States than there used to be; they have been largely replaced by Walmart and other discount stores. The net economic effect is that a lot of money that would have circulated locally leaves the community. Amazon is the next evolution in this economic assault.

In Australia, we might call it the Bunnings effect. That's familiar to me because my neighbour growing up, Mr Blackwell, ran the local hardware store, where you could get any obscure bolt you needed and advice on how to install it. When you bought things at Blackwells, the profits were spent in the community. The profits at a modern Bunnings go to the head office, which isn't your regional centre or suburb. This results in less money spent where you live. This, as Mitchell points out, is the origin of a lot of the wealth disparities we are seeing in our societies: too many people on low wages working for centralised profit machines that strip money from communities.

In an economic knife fight, those with access to capital and capital markets can beat local economies every time.

Of course, the worst possible offender is the fossil-fuel industry. Every time someone buys petrol, 99 cents out of each dollar leaves the community on a one-way ticket without creating community employment or community gain. We won't solve the Bunnings problem overnight, but we now have a viable alternative to the economic strip-mining of our communities that is our reliance on fossil fuels.

I have the numbers on hand for my own community of postcode 2515, on the traditional land of the Dharawal, now the suburbs of Clifton, Coledale, Wombarra, Scarborough, Austinmer and Thirroul, with a population of about 11,000 people. In 2020, the average household was spending nearly $5000 a year on energy, $3400 of that on petrol and diesel, $1000 on electricity from the grid, and $400–500 on natural gas. The great majority of this money leaves the town. How fossil fuels erode community is easiest to illustrate in the case of vehicle fuels. No petrol or diesel is produced in 2515; none is refined in 2515. There are only two retail petrol stations where it is sold, and one of them is more of an old-fashioned mechanic's shop full of the proprietor's vintage cars, with only two pumps selling fuel. The main petrol station does a brisk business in slushies and cigarettes, making it possible to buy three things that can kill you in one place: fossil fuels, sugar and nicotine.

The same pattern applies to all the natural gas imported into the community, and much of the electricity that is piped in. Collectively, our households are spending $14 million per year on vehicle fuels and a further $6 million on fossil natural gas and fossil-generated electricity. In other words, we spend $20 million dollars annually without generating any real local jobs. More than half that money leaves Australia.

Let me be very clear about the opportunity of an all-electric future. Our community could easily generate one-third, one-half or, very ambitiously, two-thirds of all the energy it needs. We could be using our own sunshine to power our vehicles. We could be using that same sunshine to power our water heaters, space heaters and cooktops. We could be keeping the majority of the $20 million a year that currently leaves the community and spending a lot of it here locally instead.

In addition, we'd be spending even more money in the community on the contractors and tradies installing and maintaining the equipment to enable electrification. I estimate that in an all-electric future where we generate half of our own energy, we'd be keeping 12 to 15 million of those dollars in the community. We know that most households would spend those savings, and about 55 per cent would be spent in the Local Government Area, since that is the typical pattern of Australian household spending. That is pretty extraordinary: in a small coastal community with 4000 homes and 11,000 people, half a dozen public schools, a couple of RSLs and two surf clubs, we could have $7–9 million a year of extra economic activity. That translates to 50 to 100 new jobs, a bunch of cafes, new classrooms, and new and upgraded public facilities. Those investments in communities are annual, recurring every year, and amount to the biggest economic boon for Australian communities we have ever seen. It could amount to a fundamental shift in the economy, with much more money being spent locally.

Leading into the federal election, Rewiring Australia generalised these results across electorates, hoping to create a race to the top among the competing parties on electrification. We modelled the economic benefit of household electrification in marginal electorates. The idea was to illustrate that climate change issues are not at odds with economics, and that we can afford to be ambitious in our response to climate change. The results were even more dramatic than the one I present above for my community. (All the numbers are approximate.) For the 87,561 households in the federal electorate of Gilmore, we might expect to see $385 million in household savings annually, a $26 million per year investment in local jobs, and as many as 2400 jobs created in electrification. For the 71,136 households in the federal electorate of Griffith, just south of Brisbane, we see $297 million in household savings, $17 million on local jobs, and 1800 jobs. For the 59,942 households in Boothby, south of Adelaide: $259 million in money that could stay in the community rather than leave it, and $15 million on 1590 local jobs.

Much has been made of the opportunity to reshape the regions with renewable generation and new green industries – an extraordinary opportunity Australia should seize. But the even bigger economic opportunity for Australia is in our homes, and that opportunity is available immediately, and everywhere.

What about the renters?

During my road trip, and over the past eighteen months, I must have spoken at nearly a hundred different forums on electrification, community, our energy transition and climate change. The talks cover much of the same material as in this essay, *Electrify* and *The Big Switch*. What was interesting to me was the consistency of the questions that came from the audiences. In most forums, the first or second question was some variation of: What about the renters? What about social housing? What about low-income households? What about people on fixed incomes?

These are not easy questions to answer but speak to an acute awareness that it is access to capital that determines who wins. I pointed to the fact that cars are the source of most of the savings, and that renters own them, so as long as the landlord doesn't make connecting a vehicle charger impossible, they could participate. I pointed to rate-based financing schemes, such as the PACE (property assessed clean energy) program in the United States. Although not perfect, these schemes are a method for helping low- and middle-income homeowners participate more fully by using their council rates to buy the capital equipment upgrades that save them money. I cited nascent Department of Energy programs in the US that use the Loan Programs Office to finance electric utilities to install money-saving machines in low-income housing, where the machines are paid off over time against energy bills and end up being an asset owned by the bill payer.

There will be a point where the remaining set of houses connected to gas will have to support the fraying natural gas infrastructure that is supplying less gas to fewer houses, which almost certainly will lead to price increases for exactly the people who couldn't easily afford to electrify. There will be a point where the resale value of petrol and diesel vehicles will be diminished by the dominance and superiority and low cost of electric vehicles. At some point it will be hard to get a tradie to fix your gas problem because the workforce has shifted to electric. There will be a point where the petrol stations start to close, and they, not electric vehicle charging stations, will be the scarce and inconvenient infrastructure. How will we navigate our way through those politically perilous waters if we leave segments of the population behind?

This is also the underlying question that was being wrestled with in Toronto by serious people thinking seriously about problems of political economy. One of the things that excites me most about the clean energy transition is the possibility of creating a huge amount of value for people who have been left behind by industrialisation and the tech boom. Most workers have not enjoyed the enormous profits raked in by mining companies, gas corporations and tech companies. The Occupy Wall Street movement raised some important points about inequality that were ultimately brushed under the rug. We have the opportunity to do something about the stark divide I have seen widening each year in San Francisco for the past decade and a half – a very visible expression of a phenomenon happening in many places.

Australia has also been moving down this path, just perhaps at a slower pace. We have a chance to forge our own road by creating an energy ecosystem that makes the cost of living more affordable for everyone, putting money in the pockets of cash-strapped workers. Ideally, electrification halts the steep increase in heating and powering homes, and, after an initial replacement cost, keeps the outlay steady for years to come. This would be a huge relief for the approximately 30 per cent of us who are renters, as long as there were mechanisms in place to ensure the benefits were not limited to the landlords. Just as parents receive vouchers for school clothes and materials, or people are encouraged to "dine and discover," renters deserve to have an electric bike purchase defrayed or an electric vehicle subsidised. I have spoken with renters who fear that their landlords will use electrification as an excuse to raise rents, so legislators should keep that in mind or it will completely undermine the benefits.

The market has never been "free"

It bears emphasising that it is too late for the "free market" as we know it to solve climate change. If the machines that already exist in the world — all the generation infrastructure, all of our vehicles and gas-heated building stock — live out their natural lives, that will take us to an estimated 1.8°C of warming. These are known as committed emissions. This is a climate disaster, even in the best case of rapid action. The free market will move even more slowly than that as adoption curves slowly shift towards the new normal — it's likely to give us 3°C of warming, a complete nightmare. If you keep your ear to the ground on climate science, the picture rarely gets better, and the pre-print of famous climate scientist James Hansen's new paper is not just sobering, it is terrifying. To hit a 1.5°C target, we have to intervene in the market, and change many of the rules and provide incentives to shift the market faster than it otherwise would go. The kids are right when they say it is an emergency. The adults still don't listen and cite economic-rationalist-sounding arguments for going slower.

Naomi Klein pushed for tearing down a lot of capitalism in the name of climate. This is an understandable position she laid out in *This Changes Everything: Capitalism vs the Climate*. I can't completely agree. Rather, I found myself nodding along with Noam Chomsky, hardly a staunch defender of capitalism, who put his case in *The Climate Crisis and the Global Green New Deal*:

We should recognize that if global warming is an automatic conse-
quence of capitalism, we might as well say goodbye to each other. I
would like to overcome capitalism, but it's not in the relevant time
scale. Global warming basically has to be taken care of within the
framework of existing institutions, modifying them as necessary.
That's the problem we face.

I believe the problem becomes how to work with the best of what capitalism has to offer and rewrite its rules enough to get the job done, but not so
much as to irrevocably threaten those incentivised either ideologically or
economically by the capitalism we have. The key to a solution, to my mind,
is found in the first of the political orders described by Gerstle.

A major problem of the Great Depression was that the construction industry
in rural America had collapsed, which caused a huge amount of unemployment. There was a lack of liquidity in rural banks, and construction and
home loans were inhibited. Roosevelt's solution was Fannie Mae, a federal
bank that guaranteed loans made by regional banks. The federal government
was going to backstop loans made regionally to lower the risk of default for
the banks, in turn enabling them to get more money into local economies.

It was a breathtaking solution. It was tantamount to saying that pri-
vately owned residential building stock was actually *national infrastructure* that
qualified not only for special low-interest loans but also – critically – for a
credit guarantee that enabled more households to afford this new American
dream. Home ownership went from about 46 per cent in 1930 to 66 per
cent in 1980 and peaked at nearly 70 per cent in the early 2000s. The US
housing market became the largest pool of capital in the world.

As we saw earlier, the energy transition is the substitution of finance for
fuels. Fossil-fuel machines are cheap to buy but expensive to operate. If we
do it right, electric machines will be a little more expensive to buy but far
cheaper to operate. The question is how to help everyone afford them, especially those without ready access to capital.

Your household might be in the few per cent that can afford a luxury
imported vehicle – let's say, just to be provocative, a 2023 Range Rover Sport

V8, which costs $241,021 plus on-road costs. If you drive one and also express concern for climate change, you are nothing short of a planet-fucking hypocrite. If you had bought an all-electric Hyundai Kona Highlander instead for $58,000, you would have $180,000 in change with which to eliminate the rest of your carbon emissions. Installing 20 kW of solar on your home would only cost $25,000, two home batteries another $25,000, a best-in-class induction oven-cooktop combo $10,000, all-electric heating and cooling systems for an expansive house another $30,000. You would be zero-emission and have $90,000 in spare change to buy a Tesla. Or send both kids to private school. Or electrify the beach house.

That might work for a tiny fraction of Australians, but most will have to borrow the money and choose the low- and mid-market options. Borrowing money is nerve-racking for everyone, which is why we all sweat the interest rates. Common wisdom for things like solar is that it works when the payback period is five years, but that will only be the case for the maybe 50 per cent of households that have access to capital.

The next 30 per cent of households are precarious at best for financing and often score low on the credit scores critical to modern, largely automated banking. The lowest 20 per cent of households on the economic ladder either have a fixed meagre income or no income at all and have no chance of participating. Many of these households live in social housing.

We can use social housing investments to help some of our poorest housing, while bringing the quality of that housing stock up and lowering its operational cost. But we need to be committed to that idea, as we need to be committed to an idea for the households of middle Australia.

I'm not an economist or politician, but I am good with numbers and am an engineer and occasional scientist. It looks to me like the investment case for the government to front the money to help all Australian households join the zero-emission future is a no-brainer. I would recommend loan guarantees as one mechanism in the critical machinery that gets us there. Just as American households became the infrastructure of the national wealth of the United States in the latter half of the twentieth century with the loan guarantees offered by Fannie Mae, why not extend the logic to the electric vehicles that will be the biggest battery in the future energy system, and to the rooftop solar, household appliances and heating systems?

Governor Jerry Brown of California introduced the PACE program in the United States, which enabled property owners to finance energy-efficiency upgrades against their council rates. The banks were reluctant, so he wrote a $10 million check for a loan loss reserve, in effect acting as guarantor for the program. Upon leaving office, he remarked that it was one of the best things he ever did.

With a loan guarantee, the government would only have to step in if the borrower became troubled, and Australians are famously good at paying their debts. The loan guarantees could be administered by the Clean Energy Finance Corporation or a new Office of Electrification with responsibilities like that of the US Department of Energy's Loan Programs Office (which will be administering approximately $40 billion in similar loans with stimulus from the *Inflation Reduction Act*). If only 2 per cent of homes default on the loans – and 2 per cent would be high, and highly unusual – the government would step in and pay the obligations. Using this mechanism, $1 billion can do $50 billion of climate work. The government could also buy down the interest rate a little and seek to keep loan costs reasonable.

The infrastructure analogy is important. Because of the rooftop solar revolution and the inevitability of electrification, our households are national infrastructure. Let's treat them as such, and have the best infrastructure in the world: clean, emission-free and all-electric, installed faster than a "free" market can achieve with the existing rules of the banking industry.

Just in case I haven't been clear enough, let me be very blunt. Whoever gets access to the lowest interest rates, whoever has access to capital, will win in this game of financing our zero-emission future. Large corporations have access to low-cost financing. Wealthy households, ironically, have access to low-cost financing. Companies that build infrastructure are often granted government-backed low-cost financing. Middle-income households do not get this same low cost of finance. Low-income households do not even qualify. If we do not invest in these low- and middle-income households and their energy infrastructure, we are going to widen existing inequalities, not bridge them, as well as poison the whole well. As Ben Franklin said, "We must all hang together, or assuredly we will all hang separately."

If the triumph of a political order is the acceptance of a set of ideas by all political parties, we have a long way to go. But if the foundation of a political order is a set of ideas that can promise a rising living standard to a nation's citizens, we are well on our way. Climate change is an enormous threat, but electrification is not only an answer to that threat, it is also the basis for a new, widespread prosperity – should we choose it.

MUNICIPALS: BACK TO THE FUTURE?

As our road trip continued, I would stop to take photos of electricity infrastructure. Some of it was beautiful. Some of it was not. It was, however, enlightening to observe it closely. By the river at Echuca, on the traditional lands of the Yorta Yorta, we waited for the NRMA fast charger to fill the Tesla. My mother and I sat in chairs and made pencil sketches of a particularly delightful, if confusing, set of overhead wires. Contemplating the distribution network is critical – even if artistically challenging.

When the miracle of electricity first became available, there was no place for it in the Australian Constitution, so it was left to states to figure it out. New South Wales, Queensland and Western Australia developed a municipal model: electricity companies owned and operated by city councils. Victoria, South Australia and Tasmania developed in a more integrated way, at first with private companies that were later integrated into state-wide ownership. By the 1920s, most states had evolved towards the same model of both electricity and gas networks operated as state-owned enterprises that had rolled up the previously municipally operated networks. The first two towns to adopt an electricity network, at first to support street lighting, were Tamworth (1888) and Young (1889).

The Edison vs Tesla "current war," or rather the debate about alternating current (AC) and direct current (DC), was still playing out. DC was convenient and easy over short distances but highly wasteful over long distances. AC triumphed when sending electricity a long way. AC won, and all over the world networks standardised. The first Australian transmission lines to deliver electricity over larger distances were in Tasmania in 1916, connecting Hobart to the Waddamana hydroelectric power station.

Between 1920 and the 1980s, most of the municipal networks started to overlap and then absorbed each other as they connected to become state-owned electricity providers. Different legislative decisions resulted in small differences between the states. In the '80s and '90s, Australia ran a big experiment in restructuring and privatisation of the electricity market. Then

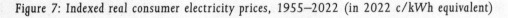
Figure 7: Indexed real consumer electricity prices, 1955–2022 (in 2022 c/kWh equivalent)

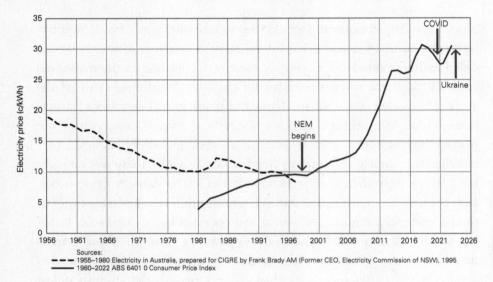

Sources:
- - - 1955–1980 Electricity in Australia, prepared for CIGRE by Frank Brady AM (Former CEO, Electricity Commission of NSW), 1995
——— 1980–2022 ABS 6401 0 Consumer Price Index

came the National Energy Market reform, where the four functions of the electricity system – generation, transmission, distribution and retail – were split from the utility monopoly to foster market competition.

Or as the ABS puts it: "Until the late 1980s, the electricity and gas supply industries were comprised of publicly owned, vertically integrated monopoly suppliers which operated in highly regulated State markets. With the establishment of the 1995 National Competition Policy (NCP), a series of reforms were introduced to deregulate and privatise these industries, resulting in significant restructuring of businesses."

Things didn't go as planned. After three decades of the cost of electricity falling, in 1985 or so it started to tick up, or at least the cost savings flattened out. Since the introduction of the National Energy Market in 1998 in response to competition policy and the privatisation of electricity, we have seen nothing but increasing prices. Some argue that this is due to the increasing amounts of renewables mandated on the grid; that used to be true but hasn't been true for a long time, with wind and solar now consistently cheaper than coal and gas. What really drove the price increases were the gold plating of distribution networks before privatisation, rising returns for retailers, and rising market concentration and vertical reintegration of generators with retailers. The rationale for privatisation was in large part to reduce the debts accumulated by governments in building and operating energy infrastructure. The subsequent increases in costs may have, in part, been due to the move to full cost recovery in accordance with the designed regulatory model.

Australia's market was never quite as "free" as the United States', but we overinvested in ideas of "market design" and got the design wrong for the world we live in today. The result is increasingly expensive electricity. It may have been a good idea at the time, but it doesn't look like a great idea now, although this does confer an advantage for Australia over the US. For the large part, the United States still has a state-owned monopoly model of electricity which disincentivises the utility from supporting distributed generation like the solar on your roof. The separation of our system into four components might look like a mistake from a cost perspective, but it is likely easier to get from here to where we want to go, which is a system that incentivises the maximum use of distributed generation and storage and flexible loads among traditional customers – households – while also incentivising competition and investment in the local distribution system.

Looking forward

What will give Australian households the cheapest electricity – and thus the lowest overall energy cost? Figure 8 charts the cost of electricity derived from the grid today – 27 cents – which can be compared to rooftop solar, at just over 4 cents. That isn't apples and oranges, you might say, because we need electricity 24/7/365. But the chart goes further and breaks costs down into components. (Stay with me here, this is important; it gets more interesting soon.)

One-third of the 27.5 c/kWh is the cost of maintaining the local distribution grid. This cost goes to the DNSP, or Distributed Network Service

Provider, which manages the local "poles and wires" that criss-cross your town. Another third is the wholesale cost of the electricity, the money that goes to the generators, be they wind farms, solar farms, coal plants, gas plants or even hydroelectricity stations. It is the average 24/7/365 price, and as you can imagine, it varies a lot by source, with renewables, and by time of day. A couple of cents per kilowatt hour is for the TNSP, or Transmission Network Service Provider – the big transmission lines that bring electricity from the regions to the cities and across the countryside. It is likely that this goes up into the future with the relatively expensive build-out of the transmission network required to connect all the renewable electricity we will generate. This transmission was the main target of the Rewiring the Nation promise of the Labor government as it went into the 2022 election. About 3 c/kWh is the charge of the retailers for the arbitrage they do keeping all the different generators maintaining the system. Two and a half cents goes towards environmental policies, a surcharge to run government programs that save energy and support further development of renewable energy. Finally, about a cent goes to reading and maintaining the meters.

That explains the first bar of the figure – the average cost of retailed electricity – but from here on is where it gets intriguing. The second column, the cheapest electricity in the country, and perhaps the world, is the estimated cost of Australian rooftop solar. This solar miracle came about through enlightened policy, clever certification, training and workforce development, continued technological innovation, industrial scale and, yes, some luck. At 4 c/kWh, it's about one-third to one-fifth of what rooftop solar costs in the United States.

You might complain that electricity backed by renewables can't be twenty-four hours a day, and to an extent you'd be right, which is why we have the third and fourth columns. These show your average daily price of electricity with current battery prices depending on how good a job you do of managing all your loads to be charged and used when the sun is shining. If you only need to store one-third, because you are charging the car and heating your water during the day, it pencils at about half of the

Figure 8: *Australian household energy use – current fossil-fuel mix versus electrified household*

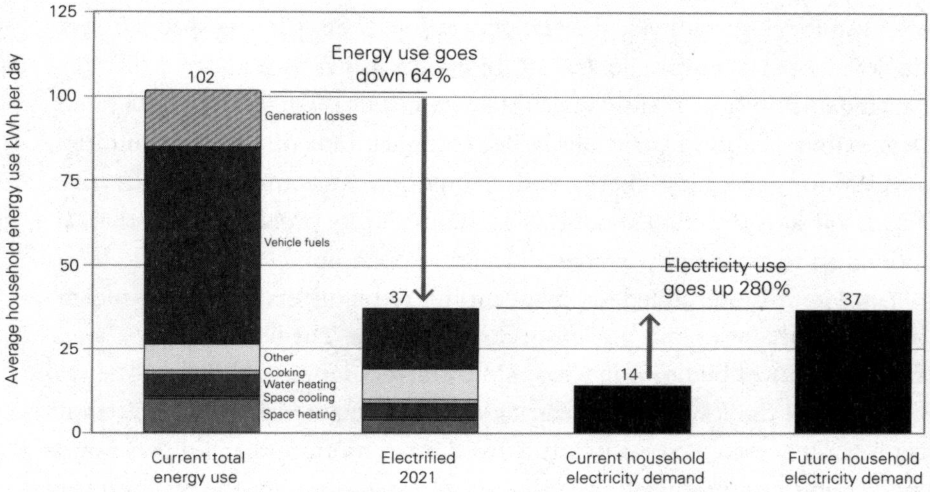

Source: Castles and Cars technical study 2021, Rewiring Australia.

grid cost. If you need to store two-thirds of that sunshine to run the house and charge the cars in the dark, you'll pay just under what you currently pay from the grid.

This has very important implications. The first is that we have crossed a magic threshold where battery-backed solar is cheaper than the grid in most of Australia. The second is that this cost is only going to fall further, because batteries and solar will continue to get cheaper because of technological innovation cycles and industrial scale. (This is not true of fossil fuels, as the resources are getting more expensive to extract.) The third is that we are developing better technologies to manage our loads through demand response, which will be managed by the local distribution grid talking to the Home Energy Management Systems (HEMS) that will dial up or down the charge on the car, move the time when the hot water heater and the battery get charged up, perhaps schedule when the washer and dryer run.

The fifth column makes things even more interesting. There are large amounts of real estate in every community, even congested city ones, that are ideal for community-scale solar generation. Every parking space or parking lot is a perfect example. In fact, in France it is now mandated that new parking lots must be planned with solar over them. There are school buildings, railway stations, surf clubs, RSLs, churches and commercial buildings, all ideal for generating energy and income for the community with solar. When we start thinking about this as a community problem rather than an individual responsibility, whole new spaces open up.

Lest I be misinterpreted, I don't want this to be understood as the recommendation that everyone go "off-grid." Far from it. The benefits in resilience and reliability of being connected to the network are just too great. The real point is that the lowest-cost electricity system for the Australian household is most likely going to be a mix that maximises rooftop solar, followed by as much community generation as the city can support, with the rest provided from our traditional transmission network connected to regional renewables.

More electrons will make the (distribution) grid cheaper

Figure 9 summarises the energy use of an Australian home today compared to when it is entirely electrified. All told, when electrified, an Australian home will need about 37 kWh of electricity daily, compared to about 14 kWh today, an increase of about 280 per cent. Not all that electricity has to be delivered through the switchboard to that house, as a little, some or a lot of the vehicle charging will be done away from home. Either way, we need more electricity delivered over local wires, and if we assume that about half of the vehicle kilometres will be charged at home and half elsewhere, this would result in about a doubling of electricity delivered over the local wires.

I still think it is marvellous to contemplate this graph. We spent fifty years running programs to make our homes and cars more efficient, but the biggest possible efficiency win we can get is electrifying everything and powering it with renewables. We couldn't see the forest for the trees;

Figure 9: Grid electricity price breakdown versus financed rooftop solar and community solar

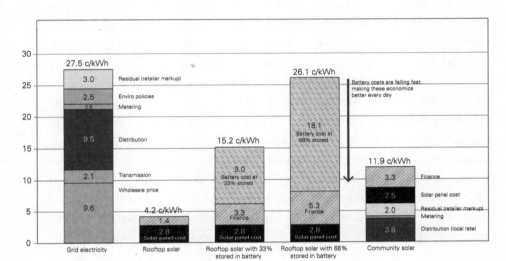

Source: AEMC Price Trends 2021. SolarChoice. SolarAnalytics. Capacity factor 17.14 per cent. Finance 4 per cent over lifetime.

we were so focused on marginally improving the efficiency of gas appliances and petrol vehicles that we couldn't envision using a different system entirely. (This metaphor applies to more than just the energy grid, as I will explain later.)

Most electricity grids never run at full capacity. Full capacity is when every single light bulb, every appliance and every air conditioner in the neighbourhood is being run at once. This never actually happens. Local distribution grids are designed around peak anticipated loads. This means that year-round, on average, the grid is only delivering 15 to 35 per cent of the energy it could deliver. If we pushed these grids over 100 per cent for a sustained period of time, the wires would get hot and it would create problems.

The bad news is that if we are to add all of that electrification on to our existing grids, we will need to manage all those loads so we don't end up in a situation where everyone comes home at 6 pm, plugs in two electric cars to charge, turns on the air conditioners and starts cooking on an electric stove and crashes the local distribution network. We will need HEMS to move the loads around, we'll need to encourage daytime vehicle charging, often at workplaces and in public spaces, and we'll need batteries, both the chemical kind and by using your water heater and even the temperature controls on the house, to store some of that electricity thermally in water and air.

The good news is we only need to deliver 200 to 260 per cent of the electricity, which means that, if well managed, our grids won't need huge upgrades to support all this electrification. The even better news is that because we are delivering more than double the electricity over the same wires, we might expect the cost of distribution to go down by as much as half, because we are delivering twice as much electricity for the same capital investment. Counterintuitively, our electricity prices might drop because we are amortising more electrons on a similar amount of wire, and this particularly hits the largest component of our electricity bill, the distribution component. I have been working with four different distribution networks around Australia this year on deploying mass electrification in communities, and the technicians and CEOs agree: this is doable, and if we do it right we can drop the price of electricity for most, if not all, Australians.

Energy management

The only precarious moment for my mother and me, vehicle charging–wise, was at the South Australia–Victoria border. The public trickle-charging station we were betting on was out of order. A phone app suggested a nearby winery had a charger. We arrived and it too was out of order. I went to the cellar door to investigate, but the cellar was closed. Moments later, the son of the winemaker emerged, a man about my age. He had seen our fancy red Tesla and had come to ask questions and investigate. I told him of my interest in electrification and he proudly showed me the two giant solar installations on the farm, the enormous battery in a shipping container he had installed to run the whole plant off-grid, and the various control systems he used to shunt the energy around throughout the day and manage keeping everything cool and charged. He plugged me into the shipping container for an extra-fast charge and gave me a tour of the winery's total electrification. It was an extraordinary display of everyday ingenuity, and the free vehicle charge and glass of wine he provided were an extraordinary display of generosity. Later we would meet his father, the property owner, who expressed great scepticism about the whole electrifying trend, and about climate change itself. Nothing emphasised the generational change around climate more than this father and son, the elder resisting change, the younger ignoring his father and making the whole farm run cheaper, better and cleaner.

The key to the winery working was batteries and energy management. More generally, Figure 9 tells the story of what we need to do to coordinate appliances, vehicles, households and solar energy. The topmost graph shows the individual loads in a home. The dishwasher runs in the evening; the clothes dryer runs in the morning; the refrigerator compressor runs periodically throughout the day; the lights are on mostly in the evening, dull overnight, and then when people wake up in the morning again; the cook-top fires up for breakfast, a light lunch, dinner for the kids, reheating dinner for a tired parent; the heater turns on a couple of times in the evening and night; the air conditioner briefly cools the home office in the late afternoon. Every home is different, and things will be on and off at different times of day, but we can look at a collection of homes to understand the average problem that the grid has to deal with.

The second graph in the figure is data from 100 homes averaged: you'll notice that all the peaks from the first chart go away, because not everyone's heating systems or lights fire up at the same moment. A collection of homes shows exactly what you would expect: we use more energy in our households in the morning when we are preparing for the day, there is a lull in the middle, and then a big increase in the evening when everyone gets home from school, work or play. It dies down overnight to the maintenance loads of a few lights and a little heating or cooling, only to ramp up again the next day. There's more heating and light in winter, more cooling and refrigeration in the summer.

The third graph in the figure takes the data from Figure 9 and projects what our collective households will look like when we all electrify, including our vehicles. We base the shapes of these curves on vehicle-charging behaviours that have been observed in the United States and on a sample set of how 36,000 homes use electricity in everything from their heating systems to their toasters and gaming consoles. We can see there is much more electricity being used, particularly by the cars. The solar systems could be larger to take more of this load, but that doesn't change the times of day that the solar will be generating. The challenge for Australia's electricity system is encompassed in this one image and the next: how many of the things that we do can we squeeze into the "solar window"?

In the perfect world, we'd charge all our cars during this solar window, heat our water during the day, pre-heat or pre-cool our homes when it is sunny and keep the heat until later in well-insulated homes. We would schedule the washers and dryers to run during the day and use batteries to soak up the rest of the sunshine and power the things we need to do overnight. We show this ideal behaviour in the fourth graph. Of course, we don't have to be this perfect at energy management, because the future will have much more wind on the grid, and Snowy 2.0 and other pumped hydro projects around the country will provide electricity at different times and store it in huge reservoirs for use later.

The task of this household energy management is up to a HEMS, which should talk to the distribution grid and respond as necessary to periods of high congestion or cheap electricity. Many people already do this manually; for example, California charges for electricity in two tiers, so our friends there set their electric cars to charge after midnight, and I spotted a sign on a washing machine and dryer on my last visit that said "Don't turn this on between 4 pm and 9 pm!!!" How much better will it be when the HEMS manages your household charging for you, automatically schedules the washer and dryer, and even talks to other households to coordinate your entire neighbourhood?

Figure 10: Grid electricity price breakdown versus financed rooftop solar and community solar

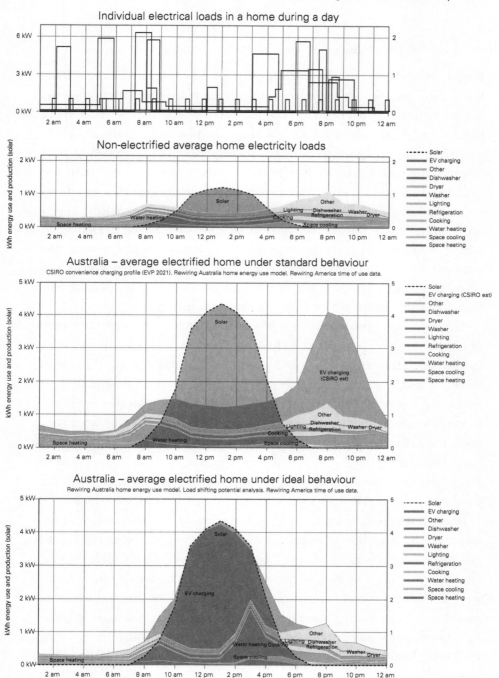

Sources: Rewiring Australia home energy use model. Rewiring America time of use data.
CSIRO convenience charging profile (EVP 2021).

Rooftop solar for the win

I need you to hold one more idea in your head before I tie all these ideas about the importance of community infrastructure together. In my community of postcode 2515, just south of Sydney, even with a majestic escarpment that robs us of late-afternoon light, we have the potential to provide all our energy for everything we do using our rooftop solar. The University of New South Wales and Australian Photovoltaics Institute estimate that postcode 2515 would produce 74.3 GWh of electricity in the course of a year from its rooftops alone. The approximately 4000 occupied households will need only two-thirds of this, or 50 GWh in an all-electric world, including to power their cars. The generation potential is probably higher because this estimate doesn't include community-generated solar in public spaces and on commercial buildings. It also uses a model of the efficiency of solar cells that is already outdated. The solar just keeps getting better.

2515 gets approximately twice as much sunshine in the summer as it does in the winter, which points to a challenge, but one way we will deal with that is over-generation. A few lucky families and rooftops in 2515 could install twice the solar capacity they strictly need, in effect designing their system for winter. They'll be producing extra in the summer they could sell to neighbours or back to the national grid. By installing twice what they need, their effective price of electricity goes up to 8–9 c/kWh, which is still only one-third of the average retail cost. We need to design the system to incentivise everyone to design not just for their average electrical load, but for their future middle-of-winter load, including their electric vehicles.

Nor will we use solar alone; there will be wind and hydroelectricity in the mix too. The challenge, of course, is winter, when the sun goes down, and during prolonged periods of rain. There are days when we couldn't power ourselves in 2515, and even with every home with a rooftop solar system, we'd still come up short in the darkest two months of the year, just when we need a little extra heating. Several things will make this a non-issue. Wind is usually stronger at night-time, and stronger in the winter, counter-correlating with solar. Wind and solar together are more reliable. Storage makes a huge difference, and we have electric cars, batteries and hydroelectricity, including Snowy 2.0, as future storage or "batteries" in the system. Finally, we need to accept that we won't be 100 per cent renewable: we need to be 150 per cent. I'll spare you the charts that make me really excited, but in a recent paper in *Nature*, one of the world's most respected journals, it was shown that with 150 per cent of the generation capacity we need, 12 hours of storage and an approximately 50/50 mix of wind and solar, Australia would have 100 per cent reliability of electricity supply all year round, or extremely close to 100 per cent. (Remember, too, that 150 per cent doesn't mean the price will go up by half, as the cost of generation is only a small piece of that 27 cents.)

This is pretty extraordinary and gels with my rudimentary models of the same phenomena. We should never have expected 100 per cent renewables to work, as we don't expect 100 per cent fossil fuels to work. Both require excess and storage. Earlier I mentioned the large gas reservoirs Australia keeps. Those, and our coal depots, are storage, and we have more generators than we need in case any are down for maintenance. What is really extraordinary is the future of abundance that this over-supply implies. With 150 per cent renewables, we get a 100 per cent reliable energy system, and 50 per cent of our energy will be excess: not quite but close to free. We'll have the luxury of figuring out what to do with that very low-cost electricity. Some will be used to make hydrogen or other "e-fuels." Some will be used as a seasonal windfall for energy-intensive industries to ramp up production. Some will pump water uphill in our huge national hydroelectric pumped storage batteries. The real point is that we need to reject fear campaigns about why it won't work and embrace an abundance agenda and an attitude of just making it work — for all of us.

Our cheapest electricity — a community energy tariff

All the pieces of the story are now in place. We know that the cheapest electricity in the future will be that on the rooftop, because it doesn't require moving electricity over great distances. The second-cheapest could be that of your neighbour, who is generating more electricity than they need, and it only has to travel a short distance down the street to you. We also know that with increased electrification we will utilise our distribution systems better and these costs will go down, which — assuming effective regulation — should lower overall costs. Additionally we know that we can build community generation assets, such as solar on our schools and public buildings, and solar over our parking spaces, and again, because that electricity is local, we know that it could be cheaper than what we have today. We also know that batteries are getting cheaper and batteries on four wheels (electric vehicles that do vehicle to grid or vehicle to home charging) are coming fast. It's an important conceptual shift to think about things such as cars and hot water tanks as batteries. We know, finally, that we will use modern control systems and HEMS to shift a bunch of those loads to the right times of day, and incentives such as cheaper car charging around noon to shift our behaviour. We also know we will generate more than we need and have giant national batteries in our pumped hydro systems.

With all of that, we can envisage a situation where one-third, and maybe even one-half, of our electricity comes from our roofs and is much cheaper than it is today. Another quarter or third might come from the local community, or more if you are in a rural location. The remainder will come from the existing and expanded national network. Even if the price of the electricity from the larger network goes up a little (but this isn't certain; it should go down), the electricity will be abundant and cheap. In fact, it will be free or close-to-free some hours of the day and during the summer months.

But that outcome isn't certain, and the existing regulatory environment and rate structures don't support it, and there is some cause for pessimism as we start to restrict feed-in tariffs for rooftop solar. I hope you can see by now that the regulatory environment is as important as the physical one. I just built an argument that a lower rate for community-generated electricity is justified because locally generated energy is cheaper for structural reasons. If we designed the system and the tariffs so that households and communities are incentivised to electrify, to play as nicely as possible with the grid, to generate the maximum amount of rooftop solar, and to soak up as much sun as they can in batteries, energy will get cheaper. This would come about by a set of policies we might call "grid neutrality," or the treatment of all generators and batteries equally and fairly, and by creating incentives that align the interests of households with the interests of the community and the city, and with the interests of the Distributed Network Service Provider. This is in the national interest. It would necessarily involve the retailers and also require their help. (It should go without saying that if we want them to play nicely, it needs to benefit them too.)

A community energy feed-in tariff would promote the use of local resources, local charging and locally built infrastructure, effectively keeping more money in a community while also minimising the costs of energy for the community. (If you don't like maths, skip the rest of this paragraph and the next. If you want to estimate a possible future electricity cost for Australians, follow along.) Using the numbers in Figure 8, we might presume that the local distribution charge is 9 cents, 5 if the prediction about higher utilisation comes true. Let's call it 7. Add a cent for management and digital billing. That would mean you could buy your neighbour's solar for their cost of generation (4 cents), maybe give them a cent of incentive (5 cents), then add the local 7 plus 1, and that would be 13 c/kWh. Locally generated solar from community assets would come in at a similar rate. Energy sourced outside the community would probably remain the same: about 27 c/kWh.

This gives insight into one possible future for Australia's energy mix and cost of electricity; a combination of your own 4 c/kWh rooftop solar, your community's 13 c/kWh for community generation, and Australia's 27 c/kWh for regionally generated and transmitted electricity. This is a screaming deal and speaks to the possibility of abundance. Using a basic model that we will get one-third of our energy from each of these sources, and that an all-electric Australian household will use 37 kWh/day, we can calculate a future cost of energy of $1980 a year, one-third of what it costs us in the fossil world of today.

I don't know exactly how to design this market and this set of tariffs, but I know that we won't evolve to the best solution fast enough if kept to the pace of change dictated by our current bureaucratic and regulatory processes. Former chief scientist Alan Finkel's great gift to Australia might have been to give us the sandbox exception. Engineers use sandboxes to test ideas, just like children do. Finkel's mechanism allows us to run experiments on pieces of the grid "sandboxed" from the sets of rules in other pieces of the grid. I am hoping that dozens of experiments in tariff structures, rate design, business models and community involvement give rise to the balance of incentives that delivers the lowest-cost energy to the Australian household. One of the sandboxes will find the right mix. The generators, DNSPs, TNSPs and retailers all have quite loud voices in the electricity market, including lobbyists and representatives on the regulatory bodies. The average punter and household is not so well represented. Neither is the community. We need to be loud about the desire of Australians and the potential for communities to participate in this bonanza.

Back to the future

The first Australian electricity grids were Municipals, or "Munis." They grew larger and agglomerated into the state and national systems we have today in various ways, privatised or not. States like Western Australia and Queensland that kept the electricity system state-owned are in a better position to align incentives with the household. States that privatised their generation and distribution systems might find themselves mediating a conflict between the foreign interests that own the wires and expect a high rate of return and the householders who would also like a high rate of return (and who vote).

The stakes are high, but what we can be sure of is the critical role of households and communities in the future of Australian energy supply. Because of physical proximity they will be the lowest-cost generators. There is a good chance we'll go back to the future and converge on community energy companies that look like a public–private partnership with a city, like the Munis of old, where the city, the electric company and the Australian household had their interests aligned.

One can't have a conversation about climate change and energy use without talking about transportation, which is principally a conversation about cars. As shown earlier in Figure 9, close to two-thirds of the electricity use of households in the future is likely to be their cars. Electric cars are the most visible thing about this energy transition and consistently the thing I was asked about most as my mother and I took our great electric road trip. We both ended up as EV ambassadors, reciting answers to the common questions posed to us everywhere we went. How far does it go on a charge? (400 kilometres.) When will the electric utes arrive? (2023/24.) Where do you charge it? (Mostly at home.) How long does it take? (A few hours a day at home, thirty minutes at a fast charger.)

The biggest emitter of CO_2 in the current Australian economy is the burning of coal for electricity production. This will end; we'll use 150 per cent renewables. The second-largest source of CO_2 is our use of cars and trucks for moving us and our stuff around. There was brief hope about twenty years ago that some of the cars would be powered with hydrogen, but as with much hope for hydrogen that has faded. Hydrogen will be more expensive and less efficient and the likelihood we will build out separate hydrogen-refuelling infrastructure and electric-charging infrastructure over the whole country is enormously unlikely. There will always be a place for some diesel, and biodiesel and new technologies will easily fill that niche. It is pretty definitive at this point: the great majority of cars will be electric.

It is irreversible

The car manufacturers are voluntarily going electric already, and sooner than you think. Many auto-companies have announced sunset dates after which they will only sell electric vehicles: Jaguar, 2025; Audi, 2026; Mini, 2026; Alfa Romeo, 2027; Rolls-Royce, 2028; Fiat, 2025–2030; Volvo, 2030; Bentley, 2030; Ford (Europe), 2030; Renault (90 per cent), 2030; Nissan, early 2030s; VW (Europe), 2035; GM, 2035; Honda, 2040; Hyundai, 2040. Seeing the writing on the wall, Europe has adopted the phase-out voluntarily. These dates keep getting pulled in, not pushed out. Toyota is bringing up the rear, part of a failed history of pro-hydrogen policy in Japan. Australia can either join the set of markets with certainty about this fossil-fuel phase-out or join the group of countries that will receive the auto industry's remainders, the fossil-fuelled vehicles it can't sell anywhere else.

They're huge. Is this how we want to tackle climate change?

I was recently loaned a Rivian R1T, one of the many new large electric pick-up trucks, SUVs and utes available in the United States. It is about 5 per cent larger than the already very large Ford Ranger. It is the fastest such truck in the world, at around 3 seconds from 0 to 100 km/h. I pushed it and could feel my brain being pressed against the back of my skull. The gigantic 128-kWh battery pack means that it can go 500 km between charges. The long-range version, with a 172-kWh battery, will go 700 km. My one weighed 3242 kg, a full tonne heavier than a Ford Ranger. Only half the weight difference can be explained by the half-ton battery. The GMC Hummer EV is a full tonne heavier again and has 1000 hp. The all-electric Ford F-150 Lightning — the F-150 is the most produced vehicle in human history, with more than 55 million on the road — is nearly a half-metre longer again.

As I drove the Rivian around northern California, I appreciated the engineering but couldn't help feel that everything about it was too much. Too big, far too powerful, too fast, too heavy, too many cup holders ... did I really need the detachable bluetooth speaker? The electrified roller-door thingy over the tray? I couldn't see a ten-year-old over the "frunk," or bonnet, in front of me. Is this how we are going to address climate change? It appears that, for Americans, this is the direction they have decided to go. On the one hand, it is great that car companies are finally getting behind zero-emission vehicles; on the other, what world are we creating?

All the wild mammals on Earth, all the whales, bison, polar bears, koalas, dingoes and bandicoots, contain an estimated 0.007 gigatonnes of carbon. That means they weigh about 35 million tonnes. That number is dwarfed by cattle, which weigh nearly ten times as much as our wildlife and represent another climate conundrum. The Tesla Cybertruck is a highly anticipated vehicle, longer and about the same weight as the Rivian. Some 1.5 million of them have been reserved in pre-orders. When (if?) those are delivered, they will weigh around 5 million tonnes. Americans buy 14 million vehicles every year, Australians 1 million. If all of Australia's 20 million cars went electric and weighed only two-thirds of the Rivian, they would weigh twice as much as all wild mammal life on Earth. Think about that as you wrap a wombat around your electric bumper. It is estimated there are 1.4 billion cars on Earth. Some people think that will grow to 2 billion. That's 2.8 trillion tonnes so far, maybe 4 trillion by 2050, one hundred times the mass of all wild mammals and ten times the weight of all mammals, including livestock. We live on Planet Car.

It is even worse than that. It takes about 3.8 tonnes of stuff to make 1 ton of car, a ratio that will go up, not down, when the cars have more copper, nickel and lithium in them, as electric cars do. And it takes 42 MJ/kg to make these vehicles, a number that will also go up with electric vehicles. At a million 2-ton vehicles a year, that means between 1 and 2 per cent of our energy is expended to make our cars, before they have even been driven a click.

And it's not just that cars are heavy, roads are heavy too. A road lane is 3.5 m wide, asphalt is typically 0.2 m thick. We have 823,000 km of roads, 350,000 km of which are paved. Assuming they average out at two lanes wide and last about fifty years, that means we are making 20 million tonnes of road every year, which accounts for another 1 per cent or so of our energy use. That doesn't include all the road base (crushed rocks) underneath the macadam. We only have asphalt as a byproduct of oil; our roads are made of fossil fuels. When they aren't, and they are made of concrete, they are still climate-culpable, as we still don't know how to make cement without making CO_2. Concrete is responsible for as much as 8 per cent of our climate emissions. All the things that support having so many vehicles, including our roads and parking spaces, make you realise that the footprint of our car habit is twice as big as we believe if we only look at the fuel consumption.

I suspect this is pissing into the wind, and that it is already too late and we will follow America headlong down a path of even bigger, even heavier and even faster all-electric vehicles. That is one kind of abundance, but let's imagine different kinds of abundance in one last hope that sanity prevails and Australia chooses at least a slightly different path. Commute time is at an all-time high. People are sitting alone for hours each week in their massive vehicles, or worse, listening to vitriolic talkback radio. While switching to an all-electric fleet is a huge improvement on the current situation, let us reflect on smaller, slower, lighter and fewer. But first an argument that will ruffle some feathers.

Cars aren't that bad

Received environmentalist wisdom is that cars are inefficient as a transport option. It is helpful to understand that this isn't exactly true. It is also helpful to understand something about the trips we take.

Let's start with how we move around. In both the United States and Australia, household transit studies are performed. Behaviour is similar enough in these two countries that we can use the more comprehensive data from the US as a proxy for here. One can take the millions of trips logged and create a histogram of trip length versus frequency. It looks like Figure 11.

The left axis shows that 1.8 per cent of trips are less than 1.6 kilometres, and 3.6 per cent of trips are 1.6 to 3.2 kilometres. You can add each of the bars up. This shows you, not surprisingly, that most trips are short. In fact, 10 per cent are 0 to 6 kilometres, 25 per cent are 0 to 13 kilometres, and 50 per cent of trips are under 30 kilometres. Because these are short trips, they are mostly local, rarely on highways or freeways, and often on congested roads. The vehicles move slowly. Average speeds in cities are often below 30 km/h. Globally it is faster to walk or ride a bicycle in many cities than to drive a car.

But since all those trips are short, even though they are the majority of trips, they are the minority of kilometres travelled. This is most easily seen in the black line, which is measured off the right axis of the graph. It shows

Figure 11: Frequency of household trips and trip lengths

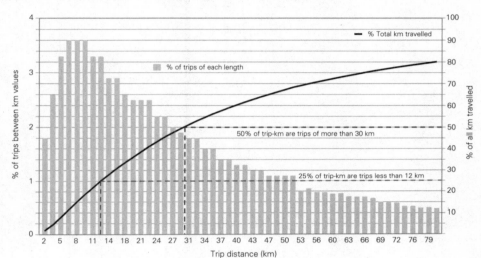

that 75 per cent of all kilometres travelled are on trips longer than 12 kilometres. Given most people don't want to walk, be on a bike or ride a scooter for more than twenty to thirty minutes at a time, it limits these modes of transit to around a 12-kilometre – very local – range.

The wonderful book *Curbing Traffic: The human case for fewer cars in our lives* details why the best solution is more walkable and bike-able cities, but we aren't going to rearrange all our cities in the next twenty-five years. As much as I love advocating for cycling and walking, we need to tackle the longer trips that are 75 per cent of our kilometres and emissions. These are the trips that require transit systems and cars. Cultural and behavioural change is much slower than climate change, so the real question is what can be done with who we are today, for the types of trips we like to take given the current layout of our cities.

To answer that question, I built a simple model for how we might do all of these trips given various (electric) vehicle options. I show in Figure 12 the energy consumption per passenger-km for a wide range of vehicles – these are the inputs to a transport energy model.

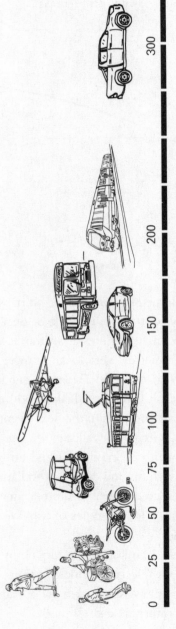

Figure 12: Energy consumption per passenger-km

Watt-hours of energy used per passenger km of various modes of (electrified) transport

As they say, mileage may vary, but you can see that electric scooters and skateboards use around 15 Wh/km at speeds up to 25 km/h. Electric bikes use around 20 to 25 Wh/km. Electric mopeds and small electric motorcycles 50 to 75 Wh/km up to around 50 km/h. A small, aerodynamic electric car like the Tesla Model 3 uses around 150 Wh/km in a real-world mix of highway and city driving. An electric SUV or ute, such as the Rivian truck or electric Toyota Hilux, requires double that: 300 Wh/km. This is hugely better than fossil-fuel vehicles: a base-model petrol Honda Civic needs the equivalent of 600 Wh/km. A diesel truck – a Hilux or Ford Ranger or Toyota Land Cruiser – needs somewhere between 750 and 1000 Wh/km equivalent.

We can add public transport to this picture. Melbourne trams are all-electric and one of the most efficient transit systems in Australia, netting out at about 100 Wh/passenger-km. Sydney trains, by comparison, are at around 150 Wh/passenger-km. Before we go any further, this leads to some remarkable conclusions.

The average occupancy of cars is around 1.4, which means that a Tesla Model 3 with 1.4 people in it is about the same per passenger-km efficiency (100 Wh/passenger-km) as our best mass transit system (Melbourne trams), and lower than Sydney trains. That is only true if it is powered by solar and wind, but if we are going 100 per cent renewable that will be the case; this should make us think bigger about what we want from our public transport systems, because the energy or emissions argument is no longer a slam dunk for mass transit as we know it.

Even the highest-utilised train systems in the world with very high occupancy, such as Singapore or Tokyo, only achieve about 50 to 75 Wh/passenger-km, the same as two or three people in a Tesla 3. Their secret is high occupancy. As I've experienced myself in Tokyo, nearly every train is standing-room-only. But for Australia it is unlikely we'll ever have the urban density to achieve those high passenger occupancy rates. I think we need more public transport for congestion, equity, land use and other reasons, but we should lead with those arguments rather than the energy savings.

A big part of the reason that bikes and skateboards and golf carts use less energy per passenger-km is the lower speed, but this is true for electric cars as well. The most efficient speed for a Tesla Model 3 is estimated to be at around 40 km/h with a miserly consumption of around 90 Wh/km, probably less if you don't have the air conditioning on. You can keep your car, but you'll have to slow down a bit, as I'll explain shortly.

We know the proportions and the lengths of the trips we want to take, and the energy consumption of each mode of travel (electric and non-electric), and even the effect of different speed limits. We can now explore some simple models to meet our transport needs. How much energy is used if we take all our trips in our current fossil-fuel cars? How does this compare to the same number of same-shaped and same-sized electric vehicles doing all the trips? What if we lower the speed limit on all the short, local trips to 40 km/h? What if most trips under 25 kilometres are on scooters, e-bikes and electric mopeds in combination with lots of public transport?

Slower is better

Figure 13 summarises the results. The biggest win, obviously, is to move from fossil-fuel vehicles (the first bar) to electric vehicles (the second bar). An all-electric-car universe can be zero-emission and also uses less than one-third of the energy of our current car fleet. The third bar models all trips in electric cars where the local traffic speed limit is 40 km/h, and the fourth is a fairly extreme mix of multi-modal electric transit, including light rail and scooters and e-bikes (and walking) for the great majority of trips under 20 kilometres. We can see that lowering the speed limit is the next "big thing" you can do after vehicle electrification, because even with all electric cars, slowing them to 40 km/h gets us a huge gain on energy use, a further reduction of about 23 per cent. Even when we model nearly 100 per cent bicycling, walking and scootering for all trips under 10 kilometres, and huge amounts of public transit and only electric vehicles for the rest, a further reduction of only about 10 per cent occurs in our extreme public transport and micro-mobility model.

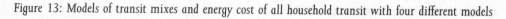
Figure 13: *Models of transit mixes and energy cost of all household transit with four different models*

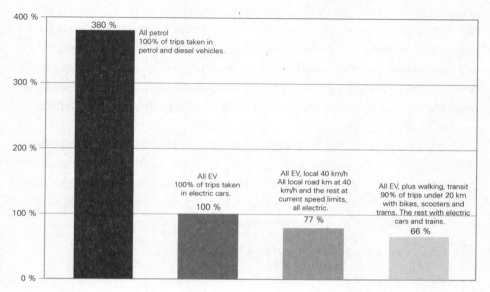

In no way is this meant to imply walking and cycling and public transport are not worth doing; they are, and for many reasons, including improved use of public space, improved public health and more equitable transport options. What it is meant to say is that we get the biggest energy and efficiency win by electrifying all of our cars, and the second-biggest win from slowing down those electric cars on local surface streets (not on major thoroughfares). It should be noted that this would also encourage and enable higher uptake of walking, cycling, e-mobility and other modes because they would be safer with a local speed limit of 40 km/h, and the increased walking and cycling would further enable higher usage of public mass transit. (Someone in a huge truck recently screamed at me that taking my daughter on my e-bike was "dangerous," though it was only dangerous because of his presence on the road!) While of course more walking is better for your health, we can see that for those who are unwilling or unable, simply driving slower brings a lot of the same benefits energy-wise.

Electric vehicles are indeed the future, but they should be part of a comprehensive transport policy that also encourages all the other smaller and lighter footprint modes, including light rail, electric buses and e-mobility. Slowing local traffic has been demonstrated to improve the safety and efficacy of all these other modes, as well as lowering the amount of energy to be dedicated to transit. Obviously it will also lower the number of batteries required for the electric vehicles and have corresponding environmental and hip-pocket benefits.

There would probably be pushback as people seem to love to terrify children as they race increasingly giant cars through quiet neighbourhoods. Perhaps we could placate the speed freaks with an increased speed limit of 120 km/h on highways, given the huge efficiency wins of the electric cars in exchange for pacifying our suburban streets?

We don't limit the horsepower of cars, why limit bicycles?

Australia has some of the most restrictive electric bicycle limits in the world: 200 watts of power and electric assistance only up to 25 km/h, compared with 500 W and 32 km/h in the United States. We shouldn't limit the power, and we definitely shouldn't limit the torque. The new electric bicycles are miraculous, and flatten the hills anywhere, but why handicap them or the rider to moving at 5–8 km/h when carrying the groceries up the hill? I think we'd be well advised to allow as much torque and power as is required to let this plethora of lightweight electric vehicles carry us up hill and down dale. Instead of limiting power, the limit should only be on the speed, so you can get up that hill at 25 km/h. Better still, increase the limit to 30 or 40 km/h, so that the speeds would match that of the vehicles and cause less frustration to all.

To make it even safer, we could adopt the European model of bicycle lanes on the inside of the parking spaces, insulating the bicycles, scooters, and mobility devices from moving traffic. I modified my own electric bike to remove the electric limits. To be clear, this is illegal. It easily does 45 km/h if I pedal hard, but that feels a bit too fast. For getting around my town, 30–35 km/h feels wonderful and is not as restrictive as the 25 km/h legal limit. I also now have far higher torque, which is very important. I live at the top of a hilly street. I frequently ride with a child (on my unmodified bikes) or with 20 kg of groceries or other cargo. With the restrictions on power, getting up the hills is difficult with heavy loads and slows the bike down to a grinding and not terribly safe 3–5 km/h. With the high power of my modified bike, I can do most of my shopping trips and conquer the hills at a reasonable speed.

Lighter is better

A number of classic vehicle models originally designed more than fifty years ago are being produced in slightly different forms today but carrying a similar spirit. The Fiat 500, for example, is a well-loved tiny cherub of a vehicle that weighed just shy of 500 kg when it was launched in the late 1950s. The 2020s electric version weighs 1300 kg, more than twice as much. Lots of other cars have also gained weight. Land Rovers were 1200 kg in the 1950s and are 2300 kg today. The vaunted Mini was 635 kg back in the day; an electric one today is 1700 kg. The F-150 at launch in 1948 weighed a little under 1500 kg; the F-150 Lightning electric at launch in 2022 weighed just over 3000 kg. Nearly all our cars have doubled in weight. Fortunately, some of that was for safety features like airbags, but yet more of it was for cupholders, electric windows, taller, wider, longer cabins and other luxuries.

Like our waistlines, cars just keep getting bigger and bigger. It doesn't have to be this way. In 1949, the Japanese government created a new category of vehicle, the Kei car. The category was designed to limit engine size, length, width, height and, consequently, weight. The vehicles enjoyed special low tax rates, lower insurance rates and special parking concessions that make them hugely popular. They have grown a little in size and weight but are still relatively tiny, at 3.4 m in length, fully 2 m shorter than that Rivian. They comprise over one-third of the Japanese auto-market.

The most popular Kei car, the Honda N-Box, weighs under 1 tonne and is a spectacularly practical van with almost Tardis-like carrying capacity.

The all-electric Nissan Sakura Kei car has a top speed of 130 km/h, by all reports is a hoot to drive and uses only 125 Wh/km to get from A to B, a quarter of what it takes to move the Rivian. I once built a Kei-class concept vehicle for Toyota that was a small van with solar covering the entire roof. It was cute as hell and would generate enough power to travel about 50 km per day for local trips at 40 km/h, a car that never needed to plug in and could run all those trips to school and the store.

It is unlikely that Australia will make full-sized electric vehicles, though maybe we will assemble some. But it would be a good idea to adopt the Kei-car standard here or write our own. They would be fantastic, inexpensive vehicles for most trips which are short and around communities and in cities. They would be safer for pedestrians and cyclists and would work well in a world with lower community speed limits. We could dedicate less of our land to parking spaces. If we were a leader instead of a follower, Australia could easily have its own industry manufacturing Kei-type cars for our domestic market, and perhaps other regional markets where US-style monster trucks aren't the only model of transport. This notion isn't completely insane: the city of Peachtree, Georgia, in the United States has 10,000 registered golf carts among its 13,000 households and an extensive network of scenic cart-paths that results in a much safer and greener suburban transit option.

Maybe you should fly?

Due to the cute piece of physics called aerodynamics it turns out that at about 110 km/h it takes more energy to keep a car safely on the road than it does to fly an aircraft. So it isn't entirely insane to talk about flying cars. I have a bunch of friends building electric aircraft. Two of the smarter ones are building clean-lined, efficient fixed-wing two-seat aircraft, one of them in Mittagong, up the road from my place in Wollongong, the other for the founder of Google. These aeroplanes are weight-sensitive, so luggage is limited, but if it is just you and your backpack they are much faster and even lower energy per passenger than a Tesla Model 3. Australia has a well-developed set of small airstrips. With today's battery technology, a

500-km range for these aircraft is easy to achieve, and it might be pushed to 1000 km or even 2000 km with solid state batteries in the future. If the outskirts of the air strips are covered in solar, they'll even produce enough energy to cover all that flying.

There is a revitalised fetishism for flying cars. They are being over-engineered to do vertical take-off and landing to satisfy their wealthy patrons with the dream they might be able to fly straight from their yacht to their office or some other billionaire-level nonsense. Back in the real world, Australia could lead the way in very efficient regional transportation by pushing electrification of fairly normal-looking small aircraft. Per passenger-km they'd be more efficient than even electric cars or super-fast trains. They don't need roads, which brings other ecosystem benefits. Their tyres won't shed nearly as many of the microplastics that fill our oceans. We could deliver more people and tourists and things to the regions, faster, in electric aircraft. What an abundant world we could live in.

Cover the medians, cover the parking spaces

The shadow of a Tesla is enough to power a Tesla. A standard parking space in Australia is about 2.4 m wide and 5.4 m long. That's 13 square metres. If it had a solar roof over it, it would generate about 4500 kWh per year. The average car in Australia does about 13,000 km per year. For an electric car like a Tesla or Nissan Leaf or Hyundai Kona, the average parking space would provide enough juice over the course of a year for 25,000 km or so. It would even produce enough power for that electric Rivian to drive 13,000 km.

There are many more parking spaces than vehicles. People live, therefore people use energy, where there are roads. Co-locating generation with vehicle parking spaces and on the medians of roads and highways will deliver the power to where it is being used at low cost. As many as half of our cars, and maybe many more, don't get parked within six metres of an electrical outlet each night. We should be putting vehicle chargers on poles. Local councils own much of the parking space in our communities. State agencies, such as the Department of Transport and Department of Education, own many more. Communities should demand that these become critical national power generation and vehicle-charging infrastructure. That is how we will minimise the cost of our car habit.

Tax the tyres

Australians use about 50 million litres of petroleum products per day. We spend $35–50 billion per year importing foreign oil. The government collects 49 cents per litre, after the various exemptions that are granted (thereby subsidising fossil fuels and emissions), which amounts to around $14 billion per year. About half of that goes to road building and transportation projects. Even so, it is not enough to pay for all our roads, and councils have to pay for much of this from their rate base.

Reforming how we pay for roads is a gnarly political problem that I think we must have some honesty about. Low-income people commute further, often in less efficient cars, and often for work. The crux of the political problem is that those who can least afford to pay for transport pay the most, and fuel excise exacerbates that problem.

People worry about how we will pay for roads once the fuel excise goes away. It is a real issue. I would like more kids to walk to school on dirt paths through forests breathing clean air and learning about ecosystems as they do so. I'd like to fly electric aircraft more and have fewer ecosystem-damaging roads. But with all that, I am not going to deny that roads are useful and we need good road infrastructure. My grandfather, after all, was the Secretary of the Department of Main Roads at his retirement.

If you study road wear, it turns out that the damage to a road is proportional to the square of the weight of a vehicle. A ute will do about seven times as much damage as a passenger car, mostly because of the extra weight. If you were designing systems to pay for our road infrastructure, it would be most scientifically done by charging by the weight of the vehicle and the number of kilometres it travels. Somewhere on my book tour around Australia, an audience member came up after a talk and suggested what we should do is tax the tyres, which would have the same effect. Heavier cars doing more kilometres go through more tyres faster. It would be a way of taxing the system that pays for roads, which would push the system to evolve to smaller, lighter vehicles. That would be a good thing. I don't know specifically if a tyre tax is the best way, but I would emphatically agree with promoting more smaller, lighter vehicles, including light electric aircraft.

Communities as laboratories

In my beachside community, all the kids are riding electric bikes with big balloon tyres: brands like Ampd Brothers, Super73, Murf. They are almost all illegal under the existing road rules, yet they are undeniably zero-emission and fun and allow the kids freedom of movement. They have surfboard racks and I see two or three teens at a time riding hither and thither making the most of their lives. We adults can learn from them. They aren't letting the status quo get in the way of imagining and living a better zero-carbon life. Wouldn't it be great if we collectively followed these examples and enabled a Cambrian explosion of these punk-rock ground-up electric transit solutions to create a better Australia? If communities are strangled by transit and road regulations from federal and state governments, we will limit our chances of evolving better solutions. We should allow councils to "sandbox" local micro-mobility rules so we can innovate new models of transit faster.

Even better, we could be a nation of big ideas about improving quality of life while addressing climate change and energy issues. To get the ball rolling, what about an around-Australia solar-electric-bicycle-path-and-fruit-orchard network? Hear me out.

It is around 15,000 km to circumnavigate Australia by car. There are already examples of solar installations over bicycle paths. A generous two-way bicycle path would be about 3 to 4 metres wide. That would result in about 50,000,000 square metres of solar installation, that averaged out across our giant continent would produce about 200 watts nominal per square metre. That would create an incredible 10 GW solar installation that would provide around 17.5 TWh per year of electricity, or about 10 per cent of our current consumption, or what might be about 3 to 5 per cent of our future expanded consumption once we have electrified all of the things. As a bonus – and I don't get credit for this idea, it should go to Damon Gameau – we should plant fruit trees along the side of this pathway so that there is frequently an apple, pear or peach for the lucky cyclist or scooter or e-mobility user.

A shaded pedestrian and cyclist facility that circumnavigates a continent, with free fruit, which pays for itself by generating a substantial portion of the country's energy: now that is an abundance agenda. Imagine the tourism. Towns would be competing to route the path through their main streets. Tourists could arrive in Australia on airplanes powered with seaweed-generated biofuels and catch an electric plane to a regional city such as Moruya, where they could jump on electric bicycles and ride to Adelaide, staying at local accommodation and putting money into local economies along the way. That would be a lucky country.

In Beechworth, my mother and I wound up at a community battery and renewable energy event at the community showgrounds. The local car club was there with their various hot rods, grizzled (mostly) men with all manner of fun vehicles. I was among my people; you see, my hypocrisy is that I am secretly a lover of old cars. I chatted with them about my own eccentric vintage collection: five of them with an average age of over sixty years: a '61 Lincoln Continental, a '59 VW Beetle with a Manx dune-buggy shell, a '57 Fiat Multipla, a '58 BMW Isetta and a '63 Land Rover.

After I'd established my credibility, they didn't want to talk about engines but how I was going to electrify these vintage lovelies. It turns out they care more about the nostalgic shapes of the sheet metal, and more about the camaraderie of turning a wrench with mates, than about whether or not the car burns fossil fuels. The idea that got them even more animated was that if they electrified their vintage car, it could be the back-up battery for their house. These cars sit around most of the time as trophy pieces, so they might as well be stabilising the community grid and making their home more energy-independent! We could be driving our energy resilience around on weekends!

While riding the coattails of Helen Haines on a whirlwind tour of Indi, I found myself at the Battery Fever! event in Beechworth, on Waveroo land, where I met Juliette Millbank of Totally Renewable Yackandandah. Juliette, an engineer by training, was leading the on-the-ground transformation of "Yack" and made a compelling case for community batteries, community solar and community energy. As would become a theme on the 10,000 kilometres of travel I did that year, the action on the ground, the organising force of Australian sustainability, were these highly effective people rolling up their sleeves and doing it, from the ground up, in their communities. Juliette presented on the technical and economic aspects of the battery and answered the community's questions on the how, what, when, where and why.

The experience of meeting women like Juliette made me reflect on power and action on climate in Australia. It was men in grey suits who broke everything. If it's true that you cannot solve a problem with the same thinking that created it, then we need a different kind of leadership this time. While men absolutely must be part of the solution to climate change, this time women must lead. The good news: they are already doing so.

Talking with my mother helped me realise how much Australia's rural development shaped its national character. She explained there had been a shortage of women for the first century of white settlement. Women were often starting completely fresh, cut off from their traditional family structures and extended family help. They had to be incredibly resilient and self-sufficient and had an unusual amount of control over their lives in many cases, as their partners were out for days or weeks at a time overseeing livestock. Women ran households that were often remote, and managed finances when their men were at war or working away from home shearing or mining. The School of the Air meant that country women could access education for their children, and by extension themselves as they supervised.

Women fought to gain entry to Australia's prestigious universities and enrolled, beginning in 1879. These capable women organised groups such as the Women's Suffrage League and the Woman's Christian Temperance Union as a way of gaining a political voice for a range of social values that they felt were unrepresented in parliament. Women in South Australia placed their first votes in 1894; voting at the federal level came in 1902, making Australia the second nation in the world where women won that right. America didn't follow for nearly twenty years. Women played a powerful role in Australian labour history as well, founding the first women's trade union in 1882. Mum recounted how, as secretary of the Art Teachers Association in the 1970s, she spoke out for equal pay.

Today, we find women leading our community-based climate solutions. The men make the headlines still, but the women are doing most of the work. They have left their egos and V8s at the door and are fighting for their constituents and communities. It made complete sense. Women had civilised the young colony and were continuing the tradition.

Among the many female leaders I met on the second leg of my tour was Christine Milne. I had already met her over Zoom, after I returned to Australia in late 2020 as a political neophyte. I was still in the midst of the IRA legislation in the US and trying to imagine how we could get the same sort of massive climate legislation to happen here. Christine was delightfully candid as she recounted where all the bodies were buried after the preceding decades of failed Australian climate policy. In Tasmania, we had a long breakfast with Bob Brown. We talked about all the things worth saving in Tasmania and Australia's great wildernesses, as well as some political strategy. I'm still affected by Christine's wisdom and humility and the obvious concern she had for this country and for the trauma climate change is inflicting on it.

Leading up to the Teal Wave of the 2022 election, I had the good fortune of meeting the impressive independent candidates – Kate Chaney, Allegra Spender, Kylea Tink, Zoe Daniel, Sophie Scamps, Monique Ryan – on panels or in Zoom calls, where we would talk about electrification and the opportunities for climate action in their communities. Without exception I was inspired by these women, who to my mind are just the right type of politicians, ones who came to politics reluctantly and to create the change they and their communities wanted but were not getting from the major parties. Each had a particular passion for climate solutions, whether it was Kylea's eagerness for zero-emission vehicles policy or Dr Ryan's concerns about the health effects of fossil fuels and climate change. Australia is lucky to have these women.

Australia is also lucky to have other female politicians who are pushing the electrification agenda. Alison Byrnes is the energetic federal representative (Labor) for Cunningham, within which sits postcode 2515 and Wollongong. She listens to and trusts experts and has the existential challenge (for Wollongong) of how to transition the steel industry, and what to do with the port facilities as coal exports inevitably shrink. I've watched Allison absorb the concerns of these critical industries and plan with them their timelines for emissions reduction.

I met Amanda Findley, mayor of Shoalhaven, to talk about electrification. She gets it completely, and her daughter is a sparkie. Amanda was very focused on how to achieve electrification for social housing. She was already thinking big about how to rebuild a more robust grid in the face of the challenges posed by the bushfires that so affected (and will affect) her region.

I met the lord mayor of Newcastle, Nuatali Nelmes, at an event hosted by ICLEI Local Governments for Sustainability (ICLEI Oceania). Like Wollongong, Newcastle has heavy industries and an export-heavy port, and the implementation of climate solutions is existential for it. Nuatali was as engaged as anyone I have met on the local solutions to climate for her community and was leading a group of Australian mayors on a journey to find the most impactful actions they could take.

I've met impressive businesswomen, too, who are innovating climate solutions. Katherine McConnell runs Brighte, a company that helps homes finance construction projects that lower their emissions while also helping tradies find jobs and ease their cashflow challenges. She is a very smart entrepreneur focused on ground-level implementation. She understands that getting it done is about finance, and about tradies, and about helping households connect to both. Brighte manages cutting-edge programs for governments, including the ACT's cutting-edge Sustainable Household Scheme. Katherine is relentlessly pragmatic about what governments can and can't do well.

Hepburn Energy (formerly Hepburn Wind) is a community-owned company run by three women. Taryn Lane is the manager and I watched as she outlined to audiences the positive economic effects of the community-owned energy collective: the jobs and the lower energy bills locally. It is a very different kind of organisation, which has made all of its founding documents and methods and accounts open-source, so that other communities can follow in its footsteps and learn. Not satisfied with the energy products on offer, Hepburn Energy created what it wanted for its community and integrated community ownership.

Non-profit organisations also have a role to play. When I first arrived back in Australia, I read about Emma and David Pocock and their passion for climate action and the organisation FrontRunners, which Emma founded to engage Australian sports heroes in climate advocacy. I too felt that climate advocacy had to move beyond scientists and radical activists, so I invited them to my mother's house in southern Sydney for breakfast. (This was before David ran for and won a Senate seat.) Through Emma and her organisation, I met other Australian sportspeople who are changing minds in their sporting communities, in this case sporting ones. Sportspeople have enormous cultural weight in Australia and are the ambassadors we need to bring climate action to every community.

In my own neighbourhood, there are climate activists everywhere. Yael Stone, who plays a criminal in the acclaimed drama *Orange Is the New Black*, lives down the road in northern Wollongong, on Dharawal land, and is passionate about climate solutions. She has created a non-profit, Hi Neighbour, and its work is grounded in dignity and justice for a community which has a long and proud history in coal and steel. Disrespecting this history has resulted in social dislocation and been a barrier to support for decarbonisation. Yael is passionate about creating "TLC," or technical low carbon, jobs through retraining and upskilling. I share her belief, though she expresses it better, that the job opportunities that come with decarbonisation should be kept local where possible.

Down the street from me in Austinmer lives Claire O'Rourke, whose new book *Together We Can: Everyday Australians doing amazing things to give our planet a future* focuses on what people can do to make a difference. She works with the Sunrise Project as Co-Director of the Australia Energy Transformation Program and is a powerful communicator on all issues climate issues.

Mithra Cox is on the city council for Wollongong and is passionate about climate solutions and bike-friendly and people-friendly cities. A few weeks after we met, she went a little bit viral in our corner of the woods for taking on some of the less enlightened members of council when she presented a motion to "electrify everything" and phase out gas. She gave an extraordinary floor speech, outlining the case for electrification, the opportunities and the technologies. She ultimately prevailed in her fight.

We need another Country Women's Association

Meeting so many female climate warriors on the road made my mother and me contemplate the Country Women's Association, many members of which we met along the way. This was progress with a side of cucumber sandwiches and lamingtons – peace offerings for local diplomacy.

I believe the future for roll-up-your-sleeves climate action looks more like the CWA than it does traditional environmental organisations. The environmental organisations that have been built in the past few decades are mostly about blocking and complaining, stopping mines and chaining themselves to fences. They have absolutely played an important role in changing the cultural conversation, but the Country Women's Association organises to get things done on a practical level. To be clear, I mean the CWA both literally and figuratively – not only the wonderful women who gave us painted lines on roads and brought civic leadership to rural Australia, but all our community groups and community organisers: the people who keep the surf life-saving clubs running, the volunteer fire brigades operational, who staff the RSL clubs and churches of Australia. Our community institutions.

I'm very conscious, however, of the trap of volunteerism. On the one hand, I love volunteers and volunteering; on the other, it is unpaid work — too much of which is already done by women. My friend Andrea Persico, who works on electrifying Tasmania, hammered this important point home. We really need this to become a paid job in every community: an electrification ambassador steadily working within every community building consensus, making plans, easing fears and anxieties, connecting the dots and representing for everyone.

There are 2644 postal areas in Australia. Organisationally, there is an enormous amount to do in every one of these suburbs and towns to get to zero emissions. We need something different from the status quo. It is already taking shape, as evidenced by the women mentioned above who are the organising force for climate action in these communities. We need something like a New Country Women's Association: local, distributed, community-oriented — and while of course it doesn't have to be women-led, my experience on the ground tells me that it will be.

The Extinction Rebellion Rebellion

I moved to the United States when I was twenty-five and spent more than twenty years there, the first six in Cambridge, outside Boston, and the rest in the Bay Area, where I built a home and business in San Francisco. The year 2020 wasn't great for anyone, but the school closures and restrictions in San Francisco made it a particularly difficult place to live. We were fortunate enough to have the option of relocating to Australia, and somewhat battered by the frustrations we had living in San Francisco we plumped for something less congested and decided to locate ourselves in Wollongong.

Not long after this, some locals heard me on the TV or radio and asked to meet. When we got together, I found they were a delightful set of young parents with about a dozen kids between them. All of them had been loosely involved with Extinction Rebellion, a peaceful direct-action climate movement that had its origins in the UK. They admitted that perhaps it wasn't easy to drag your kids along to protests at night, or to events where everyone got chained to a fence. What could they do while raising families to help make a difference on climate?

I came to call them the Extinction Rebellion Rebellion, a title I'm sure they would recoil from. I told them how no Australian community was really on track to electrify and decarbonise, so why shouldn't we see if we could make our postcode, 2515, Australia's first all-electric zero-emission community? These are everyday community members with kids, with jobs, wanting to do something to improve the climate outlook. What Kristen, Trent, Laura, Jessie, Francis, Ali, Davin, Tim, Jeremy and Tom achieved in less than a year is impressive. They have organised three community events on electrification, two for the general public and the third for local business owners. They ran a campaign to sign up households to participate in a pilot that they are helping design with my colleagues at Rewiring Australia. They are creating media and how-tos and have become a trusted source of knowledge-sharing for a community that is more than a little bit curious about climate solutions. In a matter of weeks, 1500-odd households out of approximately 4000 in the postcode expressed interest in participating in a trial that would push the technical limits of our distribution grid systems and provide a proving ground for the suite of technologies and practical solutions that we'll need to get to zero.

My stepmother-in-law has a laptop sticker that says "No one is coming. It's up to us." She founded an organisation called Code for America that is about creating digital services and online tools to make government work better. I agree with her laptop. If we wait for government, we'll wait too long as regards climate, so we need to roll up our sleeves and do it ourselves (or even better, by rolling up our sleeves, get government to back us).

This is the journey that the Electrify 2515 crew set out on. Electrify 2515 stickers are on every electric bike and telephone pole in the neighbourhood, as well as on car bumpers. They printed posters that are in most storefronts. They bought every blank T-shirt from every op shop from Sutherland to Albion Park and silk-screened an Electrify 2515 logo with the hand-drawn lightning bolt I use in my public talks. I see kids and parents at all the local spots advertising this burgeoning community-led climate movement.

People are excited, and these ambassadors and I now offer advice and reassurance to our fellow dog walkers, beach goers and the people we run into at the IGA or the bottleshop who have questions. How can my business participate if we rent the premises? Which electric cooktop do you like the best? What do you think of the Nissan Leaf compared to the Hyundai Kona? Do I really need a heat pump water heater or will electric resistance do, as only two people live in our house? When do you think an electric ute/van/bus will be available? I got a new electric bike and I love it! Or my recent favourite: We've had the garage widened because none of the EVs were going to fit.

The group's story has been featured in local and national newspapers. People everywhere seem to have heard about it. Federal politicians told me when I was in Canberra that this gave them much higher confidence that Australia is ready for electrification and that Electrify 2515 had created a national conversation. All-electric hot water heater companies and some car companies have offered us bulk purchasing discounts, and the local solar installers and HVAC tradies are offering their services. The Lord Mayor praised the concept and promised any support that Wollongong City Council could give – we are now sitting in detailed planning meetings with the city's general manager on how to get it done. Neighbouring postcodes have asked if they could join, and we hear that other towns around the country are looking for guidance about how to do it for themselves.

Trust in community

We hear from other players in the electrification space, notably energy retailers and DNSPs, that it has been historically difficult to get people to sign on for pilots of any kind, and that people have an innate suspicion of their energy companies and these types of offerings. My father (in Sydney) called me one day to inquire whether something advertised as a NSW government energy efficiency scheme was spam or a scam. He, like many of us, is a bit jaded about the perpetual stream of "Buy solar now!" advertising.

What is extraordinary in 2515 is that we have avoided that scepticism and lack of engagement. The thing about community is that it is your neighbours: there is far more trust. When the guy you see at the butcher each week is contemplating electrifying his stove, he'll trust a neighbour's advice over an energy company's any day.

When I started advocating a pilot of whole-community electrification in postcode 2515, I found myself feeling very vulnerable. I've done numerous big technical trials and projects around the world before where we had to deliver things far more technically difficult than this, but this was my community. If we fail here, we fail our neighbours. The Electrify 2515 crew felt the same angst. We have to succeed here. These people know where we live!

What Electrify 2515 has proved more than anything else is that people want to do the right thing but there are so many conflicting messages out there they don't know who to trust. By stepping in and being patient and making the case and taking the guilt and the fear away, by answering all the little questions that they might have been embarrassed to ask in a larger forum, the group has gained the trust of a community and changed the conversation on climate solutions.

2515 is a well-off corner of the world; these volunteers, while not fabulously wealthy, have the time and energy to pour into unpaid work. Some might argue about the equity of having suburbs like this benefit first, but I hope this is putting privilege to work. Those with the time and resources are creating a model from which everyone can benefit, making it more likely that all communities can make this transition.

Electrify 2515 has been a thrill to be a part of. It feels like the beginning of something. It has demonstrated to me the power of local action and trust. It is a scalable way for us to tackle climate change, one community at a time.

To be sure, the oil and gas industry, and to a lesser extent the coal industry, are still fighting, and will fight to the death. We need to be clear about their motives, and that they continue to cast doubt on things like electric versus gas stoves, and feed anxieties such as how far electric cars will go. These industries also have the ear of government, and they will look for every handout, every dubious scheme, to squeeze every last dollar from their industry. It can no longer be claimed they don't know what is causing climate change.

The Albanese government hopes to make part of its signature climate action a "safeguard mechanism" compelling industry to lower its emissions by 30 per cent by 2030 with binding caps. It is not unreasonable policy in theory, but in practice it can be gamed, specifically by the gas industry. The mechanism is intended to make Australian industry fundamentally change its operation, and for steelmakers this means moving away from coking coal and finding other sources of heat, such as green electricity. For aluminium smelters it involves procuring yet more green electricity, as aluminium-making is already all-electric, but also finding a replacement for the carbon electrodes that burn off into CO_2 during production. I'm a metallurgist by training and I know both these changes are possible, and on track.

For the gas industry companies, change is more of an existential risk, because they don't want to imagine a future without gas. They should be getting into the electrification business and retraining their workforce and changing their business models. Instead, they would like to meet emissions caps by purchasing carbon offsets while selling fantasies about green hydrogen and carbon capture that are very unlikely to manifest in reality and even if they do succeed will be more expensive than the all-electric alternatives. This looks exactly like the delay-and-distract tactics outlined so well in Michael Mann's book The New Climate War.

The first problem is that carbon credits are difficult to validate, and indeed there is evidence of gaming the system and overestimating the actual carbon sequestered. To its credit, the government is trying to reform the carbon markets, but whether this actually works warrants close and continual scrutiny.

The second problem is that carbon capture can really only be applied on big stationary facilities such as gas generation plants, since we don't have, and no one has even imagined, ways to capture the carbon dioxide spewing out of your gas heaters and gas cooking appliances. So carbon capture simply isn't a solution for a big, profitable piece of the gas industry – sending gas to homes around the country.

The third problem is that selling the idea that hydrogen will power our cooktops or water heaters or space heaters is a lie. The gas industry gets away with this by generally associating green hydrogen as a drop-in replacement for natural gas – which it won't be. The reality is that our gas networks cannot support hydrogen because the metallurgy of our pipes is not suitable. They could support perhaps a blend of 20 per cent hydrogen and 80 per cent gas, but that won't ever get us to zero emissions and it won't make anything cheaper. Further, it is implied you will just be able to run your appliances as they are, which is not true. Hydrogen is a much smaller molecule, leaks more easily and isn't compatible with existing burners – we'd have to change all those gas appliances to new, more expensive ones.

Which brings us to some real problems – concessions the gas industry has already been granted that will make decarbonising harder. One is the disconnection and abolishment fees that the Australian Energy Regulator has allowed the gas companies to charge, courtesy of some invisible backroom lobbying that the Australian public should be enraged by.

Another is the somewhat arbitrary definition of what counts as a carbon offset. We could define a more rigorous, more robust carbon offset that achieves two goals: eliminating future emissions and providing incentives for Australian households to electrify. Let me explain each of these ideas further.

Abolish the abolishment charges

You can electrify your whole house and still receive a bill from your local gas company. Gas companies are allowed to charge a daily fee. In my area, under

Origin Energy, it is 68.25 cents per day, or about $250 per year. You can request to have it turned off, which will cost you around $100 for someone to come and turn the gas valve 90 degrees to the off position on a pipe near your meter. Those remaining pipes and valves will continue to leak a little bit. You can go one step further and "abolish" the connection, which requires the gas company to remove the pipes from your property. The Australian Energy Regulator allows gas companies to charge $1151.70, a curiously precise number, for this abolishment. The gas has been connected to my house for at least thirty years, so surely they have made enough money not to need me to pay them for the privilege of the previous home owner having gas. There was no contract that came with my house that said I owed this money. It is hidden in obscure agreements you have to talk to reluctant people over the phone about after navigating hours of complicated automated phone menus.

These fees are an outrageous imposition on Australian families trying to do the right thing and make the transition to zero-emission, all-electric homes. It could cost Australian households as much as $10 billion collectively over the next twenty years to disconnect. We paid the gas industry lots of money to create this carbon dioxide problem. We shouldn't have to pay them to stop.

A better idea for carbon offsets

Instead of giving offsets for vague promises of growing trees or developing carbon capture, let's give the proceeds to low-income households which avoid that carbon by buying electric vehicles and electric appliances. In other words, treat mitigation as an offset. If you install a gas water heater tomorrow, it will probably last twelve years, and for a typical Australian home emit 6 to 7 tonnes of carbon dioxide over that time. Similarly, a gas cooktop will emit 5 to 6 tonnes of carbon over a typical ten-year lifetime. We could value the cost of offsetting this carbon, and for each appliance apply that as an up-front discount. For appliances, this would be worth a few hundred dollars or more as a rebate, making the switch to electric far easier for working families. For an electric car, this avoided carbon is worth a few thousand dollars. Our heaviest polluters could be helping struggling Australian households to electrify and get to zero.

Pundits will say that this doesn't necessarily meet the "additionality" test – that is, some people might have chosen electric anyway, so this isn't an additional reduction. Who cares? We are now in a race. These are guaranteed reductions, whereas trees are theoretical. I'll take the bird in the hand.

There is precedent for this idea in existing NSW schemes. These look at the lifetime energy use of a new device (for example, a water heater) and assign it an energy-saving value compared to a state baseline. The energy and emissions savings are estimated over the lifetime and then turned into an up-front credit on the purchase of the item for the consumer. The scheme is even done for light bulbs. It revolves around households installing a more efficient device and then signing a document that links the energy/carbon of that device to a carbon credit company that can then sell those assigned credits.

We need to find every possible way of reducing the up-front cost of switching to all-electric homes and vehicles to make this a just transition that every household can afford.

Small-scale technology certificates (STCs) were a spectacular win for Australian solar. Let's bring into existence a mechanism that can extend this success to the rest of Australian household electrification.

From my cold, dead hands

Beyond stacking the regulatory environment to their advantage and gaming the carbon offset system with dubious credits that also advantage them, the fossil industries have other tricks up their sleeves, including the age-old favourite – the culture wars.

In the 1990s and 2000s, no vision of the future checked every box on the list of things that people wanted. As a result, most of the climate solutions of the time were some version of austerity, a rehashing of 1970s tropes of smaller, colder and less. Pioneering electric vehicles like the GM EV1 were Space Age–looking, for sure, but tiny and short-range. Most people's memory and experience of electric cooking is of a slow and frustrating resistance coil in a caravan park.

Now, in 2023, it is possible to narrate a future of zero emissions with something to replace all the things we love. We now have EVs, not just sleek sedans, but large four-wheel-drive pick-up trucks that can go the distance and not ruin the weekend. Yet there will be people who say, "You will have to pry my diesel 4x4 from my cold, dead hands."

We now have electric induction cooktops that heat faster, are easier to clean, give more control, result in a cooler kitchen and don't emit toxic gases inside your home. Yet people continue to say, "You will have to pry my gas cooktop from my cold, dead hands."

We now have electric heat pump water heaters that use one-third the energy of natural gas water heaters, and even though I don't know anyone who has a romantic relationship with their water heater, I'm sure there are some who will say, "You will have to pry my gas water heater from my cold, dead hands."

It is curious that in these days of internet outrage and culture wars, any opportunity to ridicule a climate-saving action is turned into a red-hot fight about the nasty environmentalists/liberals/Democrats/greens/social-ists/anarchists/communists/fascists/etcetera coming to steal a gas cooktop from your house. America takes this to an extreme. I spent January 2023 in a bitter fight in the media about the negative health impacts of gas stoves and the benefits of going all-electric. The research article that helped kick off the fight was co-authored by diligent Australians from the University of Sydney and a Sydney public health unit. It wound up, in typical American style, with many Republican governors and culture warriors echoing the dysfunctional American conversation about guns.

Ron DeSantis, a likely presidential nominee for 2024, tweeted, "Don't tread on Florida, and don't mess with gas stoves!" His colleague Ron Jackson, Republican house member from Texas, went one step further: "If the mani-acs in the White House come for my stove, they can pry it from my cold, dead hands." To be clear, the White House had threatened no such thing, but it is promoting consumer rebates that lower the cost of upgrading gas stoves to electric through the *Inflation Reduction Act*. A low- or middle-income household qualifies for $840, enough to bridge the "green premium" of a high-quality electric induction appliance.

Photos of New York in 1900 had fifty horse-and-carts for every car. By 1913 there were fifty cars for every horse. No one forced people to switch. At first it was because cars were novel, then it was because they were better and cheaper, then it was because the infrastructure for horses and carts became hard to support. So it will be with induction stoves and electric vehicles. The fossil-fuel industries are going to come after us with nostalgia. We need to reject this for what it is: their last dying gasp.

GOLD-PLATED BOWLOS AND ELECTRIC BARBECUES AT EVERY BEACH

I want to finish this piece near where I started, contemplating a protopia. Australia is a prototype, not only for the transformative climate action we desperately need but also for a transformative social contract that will enable that action. It might result in imperfect progress towards an unattainable utopia, but, as Roosevelt said, "The country needs and, unless I mistake its temper, the country demands bold, persistent experimentation." This will sound like shameless optimism, which I think is what we need, for pessimism is cheap and rarely makes anything happen.

About ten years ago, our family took a road trip up the west coast of Australia, from Esperance to Kalbari. I wanted to explore Australia with my wife and toddler. It's stunning country, remote and gorgeous. But the thing that struck us almost more than the sweeps of sand dunes and crystal-clear water was the fact that every town – no matter how small – had a pristine public park in the centre of town with a fantastic playground and a free barbecue. Travellers and locals rubbed shoulders as they cooked, swapping tips and stories and the occasional freshly caught fish that was too big for the fisher alone. We made quite a few people laugh with our sauteed kale, but the camaraderie made even more of an impression on us.

Australia made a choice long ago to invest in its public spaces. Many of the world-famous rock pools that dot the eastern coastline were carved and poured as part of public works programs, including those of the Great Depression. Today, they are as full of joy as ever, with families from all walks of life and backgrounds feeling the thrill of crashing waves. Our beaches and parks, a historical investment in the happiness of everyday people, are paying dividends to this day in happiness and community connection. America lets people own the land all the way to the high-water mark, and many of the best beaches are privatised. Australia didn't let that happen and our communities are better because of it. Our beautiful places are not the exclusive domain of the rich. Australia has been engaged in protopia for a while now.

My sister introduced us a few years ago to Currawong Beach Cottages in Pittwater; built in the 1940s as a union workers' holiday camp, it was intended to give workers the same access to the glories of the Northern Beaches as the yacht owners. It's a particularly beautiful site, looking out to Barrenjoey Lighthouse and nestled in a few of the gorgeous coves of Ku-ring-gai Chase National Park, accessible only by boat. After decades as a union getaway, the property was sold to developers, but then public outcry ensured it was heritage-listed and Northern Beaches Council was able to acquire it to keep it publicly accessible. A string of public-minded decisions keep it available for all.

My American wife has long marvelled at the fact that in any beach town some of the best real estate belongs to a local campground. While the sites book up long in advance during the holidays, it's still possible for most families to have an absolutely glorious extended holiday on the cheap. We have seen posh couples toasting with champagne flutes as fabulously filthy kids roam around in happy bike gangs. Australia's long holidays mean most people – even the moderately wealthy – can't afford luxurious vacations for the entire school break, so everyone makes sure to get some camping in.

Each of these incredible amenities was a public policy decision. Governments chose not to privatise beachfront, they chose to ensure workers received long holidays, union bosses took leisure time seriously. These choices helped shape the happy-go-lucky, no-worries Australian character. We have seen what happens when grind culture – a term that was coined only recently but has essentially been fuelling the American "dream" for decades, if not centuries – robs people of daily joy and connection to community.

Robert D. Putnam's *Bowling Alone* detailed decades ago how America was slowly losing its bowling clubs – its community hubs. Australia has managed to keep on bowling together, with its surf life-saving clubs, lawn bowls clubs, Men's Sheds, PCYC classes and CWA get-togethers. In our local town, the beach is full to bursting on Sunday mornings with Nippers kids racing up and down the sand, a kind of inoculation against social isolation.

Yoga classes take place in the SLSC meeting hall, school sausage sizzles are held outside the local church in which people cast their ballots on election day, and art fairs fill local schools. The social fabric, while strained in some places, remains strong, weaving different cultures and classes together. Putnam endorsed Andrew Leigh and Nick Terrell's recent book *Reconnected*, which warns of a clear long-term move away from collectivism towards individualism and isolation in Australia. Leigh and Terrell's book suggests we aren't too far gone and need to reconnect now – I couldn't agree more.

What does this have to do with electrification? With climate action? Australia is at a bit of a crossroads. We can head down America's path of internal division or we can decide to dig even deeper into the egalitarian ideals that are really what have made us "the luckiest country."

Electrification will support what we already do best: literally connecting communities, requiring conversations and compromise and openness at every level, as communities decide where to put the community battery, which municipal buildings and local businesses will put solar panels on their roofs, where the public bike and car chargers will go. We already know how to do this because our rural communities have always had connection and compromise at their heart, because kids are raised learning life-saving skills so they can help others. We can choose to let the oligarchs keep all the spoils in the upcoming new energy economy, or we can choose to let neighbours in on the win. Australia has always been at its best when it keeps the collective in sight; we have shown the world that it's possible to play on the world stage while also having a surf or a camping trip. The way we move forward with electrification will set in motion the next century of wiring ourselves together, or spark deepening isolation.

Vehicle-charging in every campground: a catalogue of nation-changing ideas

Let's finish in the spirit of Kevin Kelly's protopia and summarise some of the big ideas we could roll out in an Australian protopia, a template for other countries to follow as they struggle with their implementation of climate solutions.

We could afford a round-the-nation electric bike path with a solar shade overhead that provides 5 per cent of the country's abundant and cheap renewable energy. We could plant fruiting trees along the way so tourists and idle teenagers can grab an apple as they ride.

We could build the world's first all-electric regional airport network that brings more people to our regions as people hop-skip across the country rather than just fly between six capital cities leaving the regions quiet.

We can afford electric vehicle–charging infrastructure in every camp-ground, at every beach. We could make the choice that they are owned by city councils, which can pass through the costs and promote fairness, treating electricity as we treat water and sanitation, rather than let corpo-rations cherry-pick the best economic sites and leave charging deserts in less desirable communities.

The government could guarantee loans for electric infrastructure, including our rooftop solar, our vehicles and the equipment in our homes, guaranteeing that it is not only wealthy Australians who can afford the future we need. We need to absorb the fact that the winnings will go to whoever has access to the lowest interest rate. If the government backs infrastructure companies with low interest rates to build our future energy supply, they will take home the winnings. If the government backs every Australian household with a low interest rate, our households will be the winners.

Our TAFE system could set a precedent on training the sparkies, tradies and engineers we need to electrify the economy. We have an international success story in the public-private collaboration, certification and training schemes, and incentives that made our rooftop solar the cheapest retail energy in the world. We have it in us to do the same for HVAC, batteries, vehicle chargers, all-electric homes.

We could make all communities more beautiful, with trees, gardens and parks, so that less time is spent moving as quickly as you can through bland suburban developments. Our kids could be riding electric bikes and scooters to school through forests and on protected bicycle lanes, the electric motors making sure they can carry their books and bags up the hills.

We could set the regulatory and policy settings that govern our electricity sector such that the spoils of our cheap clean energy are shared fairly among every household, especially those that need the savings the most.

Having mined enough lithium and silicon and copper and tin and nickel and iron and aluminium for this energy transition, we could show the world how to collect all those machines at end-of-life, recycle their materials and make slightly better versions of our all-electric things each time we do. We can show the world later this century what a circular economy really looks like.

We could repurpose the 38,000 kilometres of freight rail that exists in the country with solar panels over the top and transmission lines along the corridor. This would not only create 15 to 20 per cent of the energy the country needs but do it in a way that creates technical low carbon jobs in the regions that currently drive the fossil economy, and can also drive the renewable economy.

We could use mitigation tax credits to use the value of carbon not burned by vehicles and appliances to bring that value forward in time to the point of purchase, such that our electrified future is discounted for all.

Australia can afford an abundance agenda as we reach our new protopia, and we can afford to share the spoils with all our communities. We can't afford not to.

It is time to organise and engage with our communities and get this job done. It is time that we demand of government, and of ourselves a new economic paradigm that gives priority to communities over corporations, to climate over coin.

To return to the 1932 speech by Franklin Roosevelt that I quoted earlier, let me end as he ended, at the beginning of the previous New Deal:

> We need enthusiasm, imagination and the ability to face facts, even
> unpleasant ones, bravely. We need to correct, by drastic means if nec-
> essary, the faults in our economic system from which we now suffer.

We need the courage of the young. Yours is not the task of making your way in the world, but the task of remaking the world which you will find before you. May every one of us be granted the courage, the faith and the vision to give the best that is in us to that remaking!

SOURCES AND ACKNOWLEDGEMENTS

This book would not have been written without community. It was really written in three weeks in January and I relied on my father-in-law Tim O'Reilly, wife Arwen O'Reilly Griffith, stepmother-in-law Jennifer Pahlka, mother Pamela Griffith and colleagues to contribute long passages. Thanks to them all. By name, thanks to Laura Fraser, who taught me to write fast, delete quickly and not look back; Sam Calisch, who is master of mixing numbers and words; Tim O'Reilly, for insights, quotes and historical context; Jen Pahlka, for understanding what governments can and cannot do; Josh Ellison, for crunching numbers, thinking differently, and making charts and graphs; Kate Minter, for herding chickens, both human and words; Dan Cass, thank god someone has been on the electricity policy ball in Australia; Pamela Griffith, for being a wonderful human and terrific storyteller; and Arwen, for being by my side and writing so many words and for being gentle as you critique my spelling, grammar, structure of argument, accuracy of quotes and quality of sentences. You deserve to be listed as author.

Also thanks to the people of Black Inc., who are fun to work with. Chris Feik has given me an incredible platform to agitate for faster action on climate but he also gives me unrealistic deadlines. I thank him for his tireless work helping me meet those deadlines and improving the end-product along the way.

Thanks also to Jude Rae for the wonderful portrait she did of me for the Archibald.

And finally, thanks and an apology must go to Huxley and Bronte — sorry the publisher made this due in the middle of your school holidays.

10 around 100 coalmines: Geoscience Australia, "Australia's Energy Commodity Resources 2021", Geoscience Australia website, www.ga.gov.au/digital-publication/aecr2021, accessed 5 February 2023.

10   100 million tonnes of gas from around twenty-five offshore rigs: Department of Industry, Science, Energy and Resources, *Global Resources Strategy Commodity Report: Liquefied Natural Gas*, Commonwealth of Australia, 2022.

10   a few thousand terrestrial gasfields: Geoscience Australia, "Petroleum Wells", http://dbforms.ga.gov.au/www/npm.well.search, accessed 5 February 2023.

10–11 39,000 kilometres of large-scale gas transmission pipelines: APGA, "Pipeline Facts and Figures", AGPA website, www.apga.org.au/pipeline-facts-and-figures, accessed 5 February 2023; Australian Trade Commission, "Oil and Gas", www.austrade.gov.au/ArticleDocuments/2814/Oil-and-Gas-ICR.pdf, accessed 13 February 2023.

11   Seven major storage facilities: Core Energy Group, *Gas Storage Facilities Eastern and Southern Australia*, AEMO, February 2015.

11   100,000 kilometres of natural gas distribution lines: Australian Energy Regulator, "Gas Distribution", State of the Energy Market 2010, AER.

11   gas to around 7 million homes and 300,000 businesses: Energy Networks Australia, "Reliable and Clean Gas for Australian Homes", factsheet, October 2017.

11   1.5 million homes have bottled gas: Climate News Australia, "Australia's gas supply: An overview", Climate News Australia website, https://climatenewsaustralia.com/australias-gas-supply-an-overview-core-int-graphics, accessed 13 February 2022.

11   6 million gas heaters: Energy Rating, 2021 *Residential Energy Baseline Study: Australia and New Zealand*, 18 May 2022.

11   1.2 million swimming pools: Splash, "Research shows Aussies still love pools as ownership rate rises by one per cent", Splash magazine website, www.splash-magazine.com.au/research-shows-aussies-still-love-pools-as-ownership-rate-rises-by-one-per-cent, accessed 13 February 2022.

11   4 million gas barbecues: Bright-r, "Australia, BBQ Capital of the World", Bright-r website, 11 October 2018, https://bright-r.com.au/australia-bbq-capital-of-the-world, accessed 13 February 2022.

11   131 million barrels of oil and import 842 million: Geoscience Australia, "Oil", Geoscience Australia website, www.ga.gov.au/digital-publication/aecr2021/oil, accessed 5 February 2023.

11   serious security risk: John Francis, *Australia's Fuel Security: Running on Empty*, report for the Maritime Union of Australia, November 2018, www.cfmmeu.org.au/sites/www.cfmmeu.org.au/files/2018%20MUA%20fuel%20security%20report.pdf, accessed 5 February 2023.

11   6500 petrol stations: Australian Institute of Petroleum, "Australian Oil Refineries", At a Glance information sheet, AIP, www.aip.com.au/sites/default/files/

download-files/2017-09/At%20a%20Glance%20Australian%20Oil%20Refineries.pdf, accessed 5 February 2023.

11   20 million vehicles: Department of Infrastructure, Transport, Regional Development and Tourism, "Australia's light vehicle fleet – some insights", www.bitre.gov.au/sites/default/files/documents/light-vehicles-info-sheet-108.pdf, accessed 13 February 2022.

11   500,000 rigid trucks, 105,000 articulated trucks and 97,000 buses: Australian Bureau of Statistics, *Motor Vehicle Census, Australia,* 31 January 2021.

11   2279 commercial airplanes and 9150 in our general aviation fleet: Department of Infrastructure, Transport, Regional Development and Tourism, *Australian Aircraft Activity* 2020, Statistical report, Commonwealth of Australia, 2021.

11   1 million boats: Boating Industry Association, "Boating Data Report Card Launched", BIA website, 28 July 2022, www.bia.org.au/news/boating-data-report-card-launched, accessed 5 February 2023.

14   the Norwegian government: At the moment electric vehicles are outselling hydrogen ones about 100 to 1, so that's a pretty conclusive answer to that debate.

21   cost of energy ... for a fully electrified Australian household: More details on these calculations can be seen in Rewiring Australia's household energy cost study: www.rewiringaustralia.org/report/castles-cars-technical-study.

22   Once financed and installed on your roof: assuming a twenty-year fixed interest rate.

26   not punitive as a carbon tax might have been: I am not against a carbon price, which is a better name for a carbon tax, if we call it what it is, a price – in theory it is the price of the climate destruction it will cause. A carbon price that allows that money paid for carbon to purchase things that won't produce carbon would be great.

26   the Democrats didn't have a sixty-seat, filibuster-proof majority in the Senate: Don't get me started.

27   Figure 6: The only variation in the data is around the Department of Energy's Loan Program Office program, which was allocated $3.6 billion but will be able to deploy something closer to $36 billion in capital as it involves highly leveraged loan guarantees. Further analysis can be found at the Rewiring America website, including a calculator that shows the effect of incentives to individual households throughout the United States who on average qualify for around $14,000 to electrify their homes, vehicles and appliances, including solar and batteries.

30   key metals and minerals: There are arguments to be made about the damage mining does, but nothing compares to the scale of coal and gas extraction.

30   Jesse Jenkins: Molly Seltzer, "Princeton energy and climate experts weigh in on the impact of the *Inflation Reduction Act*, Princeton University website, 25 August 2022, www.princeton.edu/news/2022/08/25/princeton-energy-and-climate-experts-weigh-impact-inflation-reduction-act, accessed 13 February 2023.

33 "Should any political party": Dwight D. Eisenhower, Letter to Edgar Newton Eisenhower, 8 November 1954, Teaching American History website, https://teachingamericanhistory.org/document/letter-to-edgar-newton-eisenhower, accessed 13 February 2023.

34 "Only a crisis": From the Preface of the 1982 20th anniversary edition of *Capitalism and Freedom*.

35 methane emissions from sheep: No small problem indeed, given the influence of sweet little lambs on the New Zealand economy and the 44 per cent of their emissions footprint they and cows represent.

38 2020 numbers: COVID and the war in Ukraine have increased energy prices since.

38 In 2020, the average household: Data is from Australian Bureau Statistics and from Australian Residential Baseline Study, as documented in the methodology of www.rewiringaustralia.org/castles-and-cars.

38 proprietor's vintage cars: When he profits from selling petrol I'm pretty sure he spends the dollars he makes maintaining and racing his vintage cars.

39 More than half that money leaves Australia: Globalpetrolprices.com, "Chart: Breakdown of gasoline prices", 6 April 2015, /www.globalpetrolprices.com/articles/19, accessed 14 February 2023.

39–40 Gilmore: Rewiring Australia, *Rewiring Southern NSW: A report on the community benefits of electrification prepared by Rewiring Australia*, www.rewiringaustralia.org/report/rewiring-southern-nsw, accessed 5 February 2023.

40 Griffith: Rewiring Australia, *Rewiring Greater Brisbane: A report on the community benefits of electrification prepared by Rewiring Australia*, www.rewiringaustralia.org/report/rewiring-greater-brisbane, accessed 5 February 2023.

40 Boothby: Rewiring Australia, *Rewiring Adelaide: A report on the community benefits of electrification prepared by Rewiring Australia*, www.rewiringaustralia.org/report/rewiring-adelaide, accessed 5 February 2023.

40 they could participate: We probably need regulation that requires landlords to install vehicle chargers at the renter's request.

42 committed emissions: Dan Tong et al., "Committed emissions from existing energy infrastructure jeopardize 1.5°C climate target", *Nature*, 1 July 2019.

42 pre-print: This isn't through peer review yet but is available on at https://arxiv.org/pdf/2212.04474.pdf.

48 "Until the late 1980s": Australian Bureau of Statistics, "Preface", *Directory of Electricity, Gas, Water and Sewerage Statistics*, 2001, 1140.0, 1 May 2001.

49 into components: Department of Climate Change, Energy, the Environment and Water, "1. Understand your energy use", www.energy.gov.au/business/energy-management-business/1-understandyour-energy-use, accessed 13 February 2022.

50 Rewiring the Nation promise: $20 billion has now been earmarked for this project, though the scope may grow larger to accommodate distributed energy resources and demand side electrification.

54 public trickle-charging station ... was out of order: In the near future there will be so many public vehicle-charging stations this will not be a problem.

56 "solar window": Some people will protest what about wind? There will be tonnes of wind, but because it will generally be remote, it will be more expensive than local solar.

58 The University of New South Wales and Australian Photovoltaics Institute estimate: Mike B. Roberts, Jessie K. Copper & Anna Bruce, "Analysis of rooftop solar potential on Australian residential buildings", Asia Pacific Solar Research conference, Sydney, December 2018.

59 recent paper in *Nature*: D. Tong et al., "Geophysical constraints on the reliability of solar and wind power worldwide", *Nature Communications* 12, 2021, p. 6146.

59 more generators than we need: Thirteen or more of our coal generators are typically down at any given moment: Colin Packham, "Some coal power capacity to return this week, aiding wholesale prices", *Australian Financial Review*, 10 May 2022.

59 huge national hydroelectric pumped storage batteries: Snowy Hydro 2.0 will have a storage capacity of around 350 GWh, which implies more than three hours of storage for an all-electric Australia, which will need roughly 100 GW for everything we do today.

60 down the street to you: I may as well put this footnote here: electrons don't actually travel down the street, they act as something more like pressure, but we measure the flows of electricity and could measure the flow from your neighbour to you. I have to have these footnotes because, historically, fastidious engineers are the people who send me handwritten letters about these details. I see you!

62 current bureaucratic and regulatory processes: There are around 800 pages of proposed rule changes to the NEM every week!

64 failed history of pro-hydrogen policy in Japan: Loz Blain, "Report: Japan 'hydrogen society' policy 'has clearly been a complete failure'", *New Atlas*, 25 January 2023.

64 gigantic 128-kWh battery pack: This is extraordinary – this car battery could power all of the needs of a typical Australian household for three and a half days, including the driving!

64   All the wild mammals on Earth: Yinon M. Bar-On, Rob Phillips and Ron Milo, "The biomass of Earth", *Proceedings of the National Academy of Sciences of the United States*, vol. 115, no. 25, pp. 6506–11.

65   3.8 tonnes of stuff to make 1 ton of car: Fernando Enzo Kenta Sato, and Toshihiko Nakata, "Energy consumption analysis for vehicle production through a material flow approach", *Energies*, vol. 13, no. 9, 2020.

65   Concrete is responsible: Guardian Australia, "Concrete: the most destructive material on Earth", podcast, 25 February 2019.

66   faster to walk or ride a bicycle: Tali Trigg, "Cities where it's faster to walk than drive", *Scientific American*, 16 May 2015.

66   Commute time: Michael Flood & Claire Barbato, *Off to Work: Commuting in Australia*, Australia Institute, Discussion Paper No. 78, April 2005.

69   electric scooters and skateboards: "How many MPGs does a Onewheel get?", Trailwheel website, https://trailwheel.com/how-many-mpgs-does-a-onewheel-get, accessed 5 February 2023.

69   Electric bikes: Bosch, "What is the average consumption of an eBike in use?", Bosch website, 5 February 2023, www.bosch-ebike.com/au/help-center/what-is-the-average-consumption-ofan-ebike-in-use-187300, accessed 5 February 2023.

69   Electric mopeds and small electric motorcycles: Micah Toll, "First look: 68 MPH (110 km/h) Sur Ron Storm Bee street-legal electric motorcycle", Elecktrek website, 22 September 2019, https://electrek.co/2019/09/22/first-look-sur-ron-storm-bee-electric-motorcycle, accessed 13 February 2023.

69   Tesla Model 3: US Department of Energy, "2021 Tesla Model 3", EPA website, www.fueleconomy.gov/feg/bymodel/2021_Tesla_Model_3.shtml, accessed 5 February 2023.

69   Rivian: US Department of Energy, "2022 Rivian R1T", EPA website, www.fueleconomy.gov/feg/noframes/44462.shtml, accessed 5 February 2023.

69   Melbourne trams: Public Transport Users Association, "Myth: Trams have more greenhouse emissions than cars", PTUA website, 3 May 2021, www.ptua.org.au/myths/tram-emissions, accessed 5 February 2023.

69   Sydney trains: NSW Department of Transport, *Sydney Trains Performance Update 2017*.

69   average occupancy of cars is around 1.4: NSW Department of Transport, *Household Travel Survey Report: Sydney 2012/13*, NSW Government Bureau of Transport Statistics, November 2014.

74   Peachtree, Georgia: David Zipper, "Why golf carts – golf carts! – are a transportation mode of the future", *Slate*, 15 August 2022.

75   tyres won't shed ... microplastics: Claire Gwinnet, "How your car sheds microplastics in the ocean thousands of miles away", *The Conversation*, 15 July 2020.

75 standard parking space: Australian / New Zealand Standards, AS/NZS 2890.1:2004, https://trafficparking.com.au/2890.1-2004(+A1).pdf

75 average car in Australia: Australian Bureau of Statistics, *Survey of Motor Vehicle Use, Australia*, ABS, 21 December 2020.

75 vehicle chargers on poles: Ausgrid, "Australia's first power pole mounted EV power charger installed in Newcastle", Ausgrid website, 20 December 2022, www.ausgrid.com.au/About-Us/News/Pole-mounted-EV-charger, accessed 5 February 2023.

76 A ute will do about seven times as much damage: www.lrrb.org/pdf/201432.pdf; Incidentally it is garbage trucks that do the most damage to local roads – we should probably lighten up on our trash too ...

77 circumnavigate Australia: Britz, "How Long Should You Travel Around Australia", Britz website, www.britz.com/au/en/get-inspired/articles-tips/how-long-should-you-travel-around-australia, accessed 13 February 2023.

84 2644 postal areas: Australian Bureau of Statistics, *Australian Statistical Geography by Standard (ASGS) Edition 3*, 6 October 2021.

92 research article: Talor Gruenwald et al., "Population attributable fraction of gas stoves and childhood asthma in the United States", *International Journal of Environmental Research and Public Health*, vol. 20, no. 1, 2023.

Christopher Pyne

In a media milieu where news ages hourly, Katharine Murphy's substantial *Lone Wolf* was both insightful and useful in understanding what drives Prime Minister Anthony Albanese.

As a keen antagonist and friend of the new prime minister, while not wishing to correct anything in the essay, I feel I can add some texture to Murphy's observations and analysis.

After most recent changes of government or even prime minister in Australia, pieces are written that suggest the new head of the government has ushered in a "new politics." It didn't feel that way in 1996, when John Howard defeated Paul Keating, largely because they were seen to be men of a similar era, having both come into politics in the late 1960s/early 1970s and become household names over the ensuing decades.

It certainly felt that way in 2007, when there was a generational change after a long period of government and the baton was passed from (or rather wrenched from the grasp of) Howard to Kevin Rudd. So too when Julia Gillard lost to Tony Abbott, mostly because they are utterly different characters.

The pattern was repeated in 2015, when Malcolm Turnbull replaced Abbott. One commentator even characterised this as ushering in a "new Camelot," apropos the Kennedy ascension in the United States in 1961! Alas, it was not to be.

I have always been sceptical of the epithet "new politics." To me, there's only the ebb and flow of victory and defeat. Each practitioner of politics works out what they need to do and the mood to tap into, in order to get elected over their rivals. It's been that way in the West since the Roman Republic. Politics is understanding human nature.

In 2022, Albanese sensed the mood better than anyone else, whether on his own side or in Scott Morrison's government, and emerged with the trophy. There's been no epochal shift in politics. The proof of that will be in how the Albanese government is judged over the coming few years. It won't be re-elected on whether it delivers an Indigenous Voice to Parliament, creates a national anti-corruption commission or mitigates the harmful effects of climate change on our society and environment. While those issues are important to many Australians, as for every government before it, the yardstick of success will be how well it manages the formidable challenges to our economic and national security.

There's something else to tease out from Murphy's important essay: how did Albanese beat more-fancied rivals to become leader of the parliamentary Labor Party and then prime minister? I'm sure that's a question they are all still asking themselves! Albanese was the outsider – destined for senior office, but not for the top of the greasy pole.

Outsiders often win in life – whether in business, politics, the arts, sport or other pursuits. The truth is, outsiders have to work harder to win. It makes them resilient. It makes them tenacious. Think about your school reunions as you get older. How often have you thought to yourself, "Whatever happened to such and such? He or she was the best-looking, most popular, sportiest kid when we were at school. Why didn't things turn out the same way for them in life?"

Fact is, when it's too easy for you in the first part of your life, it tends to inculcate a sense of entitlement that the rest of the world resents and, unless you have enough self-awareness to understand this, can often prove fatal to ultimate success.

Outsiders don't have that problem. They have to fight for every crumb. As they win, they realise quickly that the secret of success isn't relying on others or your looks or your connections; it's about what you can do with hard work, tenacity, a team and a certain *je ne sais quoi*.

Malcolm Fraser and John Howard were both outsiders in politics. Fraser was ten years on the back bench before he was promoted to the ministry. He wasn't part of the Menzian clique that ran the Victorian Liberal Party. He had to claw his way to the top, deposing John Gorton and then Billy Snedden in bloody coups before he had his chance to politically neck Gough Whitlam.

Howard, too, wasn't the favoured son of the Liberal establishment. That was Andrew Peacock. Despite Peacock challenging Fraser when he was prime minister, Fraser still supported Peacock over Howard in the leadership ballot after he lost the 1983 federal election. Howard and Peacock fought a political civil war from 1983 to 1995, culminating in Peacock retiring from the House of Representatives and Howard finally winning the top prize in March 1996.

Albanese is, as Murphy writes, a "lone wolf." He is a product of his upbringing – a single child, in a one-parent family, helping to support his chronically ill mother on not very much. He learnt to be resourceful, to fend for himself and be content with his own company.

In the Labor Party, he is an outsider. I suspect he is happy to be so. He was in a minority sub-faction of a minority faction in a political party that has spent more time in Opposition at the national level than in government. When thwarted by his rivals in the Left faction, he set about replacing them. He succeeded. He settled into his role as head of the Left and the most senior cabinet minister after the prime minister until his party ate itself and went back into Opposition after only six years in government. Then he bided his time, took no shtick from anyone and made his move when his internal opponents were bereft after the 2019 national election. He did it all on his own terms.

I first noticed him when we were both backbenchers on the outside – he in the Labor caucus and me in the Howard government. I was elected before Albanese, in 1993. He was elected in 1996. I happened to be sitting in the House of Representatives chamber when he rose to speak and delivered a blistering appraisal of the then prime minister. I was shocked but quite impressed that such a greenhorn would have the chutzpah to take on the most powerful person in the land! I immediately marked him down as a creature to watch and be wary of in the political jungle.

As it turned out, our careers were to intersect over and over again in the next two decades. For ten years we sparred in our roles as Manager of Opposition Business and Leader of the House. We even swapped offices when the change of government came in 2013. We had countless debates across the chamber and traded innumerable critiques of each other's ability. For eight years, we appeared every Friday morning on Nine's *Today* at 6 a.m. Almost always in person, which on reflection seems quite bizarre.

Over time, we came to respect and even like each other. I think I can say without conceit, there would be few on the Coalition side who know Albanese as well as I do.

I'm not surprised he won. He kept his rivals in front of him, where he could see them. In racing terms he was one back, on the outside. Others were expected to lead and did. Bill Shorten led Labor to two elections, but lost. Greg Combet and Lindsay Tanner retired. Chris Bowen wasn't favoured after Labor's 2019 defeat at the hands of Scott Morrison. Wayne Swan was associated with the schisms that racked the Rudd and Gillard governments. Tanya Plibersek and Tony Burke decided to fold their tents for the time being. Meanwhile, the outsider kept doing what he had always done: building his team, defeating his internal rivals – such as the Ferguson Left, led by Martin and Laurie Ferguson – honing his skills, letting others underestimate him and learning how to be a leader, not a rebel.

I also happened to be in the House of Representatives chamber when Albanese delivered his remarks adding to the motion of condolence following the death of his political hero and mentor, Tom Uren. I knew what Uren had meant to Albanese. I spoke to him briefly afterwards and offered him my sympathies.

Mentorship is an innate part of politics. It is a job undertaken by serving political figures to secure the future of their party – and ensure the continuation of their own political beliefs – by identifying and supporting like-minded, capable and smart future leaders.

Uren saw in Albanese a future leader, of his faction and his party. Sure, he was rough around the edges, quick to take offence, a brawler, a socialist and a rebel. But he was also articulate, committed, partisan, hardworking, passionate and believed in things. Uren – a former prisoner-of-war of the Japanese in World War II, a socialist and a committed Labor Left partisan – grasped immediately the potential of Albanese and, against the objections of some, brought him into the fold to give him a chance. Albanese pinned his ears back and ran.

Albanese had raw energy. Uren taught him how to channel that energy into making things happen. For himself and now ultimately, finally, for the country.

The parliament itself is a tool of Albanese's that his rivals underestimated and probably still do. In modern politics, some of our leaders think it fashionable to denigrate the importance of the parliament – the debates, Question Time and the legislative process. Little time is devoted to learning the mores of the House of Representatives by its members. Yet it is the crucible of our democracy. Far too much attention is afforded the importance of the "news cycle" and how the parliament fits into that, rather than the other way around. Critics regard knowledge of parliamentary procedure and an ability to debate and win in the parliament as evidence of a member of parliament being elitist or out of touch. In fact, being able to master the parliament is a potent weapon.

Having the ability to knock down your opponents in the chamber and demonstrate your superiority, by tearing holes in their argument or tripping them up on procedure, is noticed by the two most important groups in the Canberra bubble: your colleagues and the press gallery. It's how young, ambitious politicians come to the attention of their seniors, particularly among the leadership of their party.

Taking the fight up to the other side, whether in the parliament or the media, is a valued skill in politics, probably more so than in any other walk of life. Many politicians are intimidated by the House. Not Albanese. He loves it.

There is no surer way to stand out from the pack than to showcase your abilities in the one forum that every MP attends every day the House sits: Question Time. I have seen otherwise capable men and women left bewildered by what just happened to them in Question Time. They usually never recovered and were diminished in the eyes of their peers. You could almost smell their fear as the sharks of the press gallery and their rivals in the party room or caucus began to circle. Equally, a startlingly good performance in Question Time from a minister, leader or backbencher would capture the attention of the rest of the House and the press gallery and either confirm the superiority of the minister, strengthen the leader or mark a backbencher out for promotion.

Albanese, as a seasoned fighter, realised the opportunity the chamber gave him the moment he arrived as the Member for Grayndler. None of his rivals in the Labor caucus took the chamber nearly as seriously. Some were good anyway because of their strengths in debate. Others looked pedestrian.

Albanese has spent twenty of his twenty-six years in parliament in Opposition. During long years in the wilderness, the leader who can lift his or her colleagues' spirits with a withering assessment of the other side or bring down the "weak wildebeest in the herd" of the ministry is always a candidate for the award of most valued player of the year. Albanese did that more often for his side than anyone else I witnessed.

In other words, Albanese is a battle-hardened political performer. He hasn't presided over the arrival of "new politics" in Australia. Like all the winners before him in the past forty years (Hawke in 1983, Howard in 1996, Rudd in 2007, Abbott in 2013), he has played a straightforward, traditional hand – don't distract from your opponent's mistakes, present a non-threatening alternative, lead a united team, work hard and be patient.

Albanese understood the desire among Australian voters for a quiet life, rather than constant partisan political stress, and he surfed the deep unpopularity of the prime minister all the way to the Lodge. The reason this orthodoxy appears like "new politics" to some is because the fifteen years from 2007 to 2022 were so fractious and unique.

How Albanese performs as head of a government remains to be seen. The true tests start now, in 2023. Much depends on the ability of the Opposition, led by Peter Dutton, to hold him to account and apply political pressure. That's the job in our adversarial system of democracy. Whether the Liberal and National parties can regroup and reorient to a winning formula that appeals to a majority of the people by the time of the next election remains to be seen.

Both Albanese and Dutton have got off to solid starts. Both have challenges. Fortunately for Dutton, the spotlight is always on the government, unless the Opposition brings it on itself through disunity or stupidity. He has time to work out how to win back the Liberal heartland and appeal to enough aspirational

Australians to remind them why they voted for the Coalition for most of the last seventy years at the national level. But he also has to navigate two political parties that have among them many who believe the electorate needs to bend to their will rather than the other way around.

Albanese, treasurer Jim Chalmers and finance minister Katy Gallagher face serious economic headwinds – rising interest rates, rising inflation, the need to expand the workforce, a potential wages explosion, the risk of industrial unrest, slowing growth in markets such as China and the United States, the effect on Europe and elsewhere of the Russia–Ukraine War, rising energy prices and a substantial national debt and record government deficits fuelled by the necessary response to the Covid-19 pandemic.

His government also must reassure the Australian public that our national security is in safe hands. Developing the AUKUS agreement is critical and complicated. Well handled, it will strengthen the likelihood of peace in the Indo-Pacific and check the ambitions of China to expand its sometimes less than benign influence on the world. The globe is a more dangerous place today than it was five years ago. We have less time to react to changes in the military parity of the region. There is a realisation on both sides of the political divide that Australia must invest more in weaponry, platforms and people for our defence.

Seen from an economic perspective, AUKUS has the potential to continue remaking our strategic industrial base and our sophistication as an advanced manufacturing economy. Economic power is military power. They go hand in hand.

Despite his clear appeal to young people and his "log cabin" narrative, which is genuine and acknowledged by friend and foe alike, Albanese will not get re-elected on a vibe. The next election will be decided, as is every Australian election, on which party has the confidence of the Australian people to deliver a better standard of living, economic security and national security.

As a nationalist, to use his own words, I hope he has "a plan."

Christopher Pyne

Michael Cooney

Politics is both funnier and more serious than people expect, and so is *Lone Wolf*. Maybe no one in 2022 quite "campaigned in poetry," but Katharine Murphy saw the election in haiku. Think of her rendering of the unsettling prospect for any Labor handler of an unscripted lakeside conversation between the leader and a self-funded retiree.

> No hecklers have been ejected from the scene. Reality is coming in
> hot. *The country needs a change. Get this done,* the bloke says to the Labor
> leader.

Or her anxious interior dialogue later that day, moments before a photo shoot at Anthony Albanese's home.

> He's tired and I don't want to intrude. Where's the dog? Do we need
> the dog? Should we go back to the city?
> Albanese watches me … He points at the lounge. Grateful, I sit.

Twenty pages in, I texted a friend to say this was the most unexpectedly funny thing I'd found since reading *Growing Up African in Australia* in lockdown two years ago.

And it's also the most serious. Here, unlike in a lot of journalism – even journalism containing revelatory reporting – there are precise and subtle details to savour. When we read of election night, "As the night wore on, it was clear … 'I don't hold a hose, mate' was past tense," we have to think, yes, nicely done. He really didn't, did he. Later, "Albanese adores the dog … like a child" carries a lovely ambiguity which can't be an accident. And as for, "I say belief, not faith, because Albanese believes in what he can see," I don't think St Paul could have put it better.

The prime minister is also a funny man, as well as a serious one. I like that this comes through in Murphy's consideration of his character and the politics he is leading us through.

Albanese's good humour is something all his friends of forty years' standing reflect on when they speak about him. I've certainly seen it in the twenty years (goodness me) that I've worked with and – briefly – for him. People ask you what are they like, these Labor leaders. It is sometimes interesting which people ask about which leaders. The first thing I have always said about Albanese is that of all the Labor leaders I've worked for or with, and that's all of them since 1996, he's the one I'd be happiest to find sitting next to me on a flight to Perth.

I said that once, when giving the vote of thanks after he gave the Harvester Oration in late 2020, and one person laughed: the leader of the Labor Party, Anthony Albanese. I really hope that doesn't change.

But some things definitely changed about Anthony Albanese while he was Opposition leader. "The old dog for the hard road had to learn some new tricks," we read. A hundred per cent. Murphy points out that the Opposition leader had never run for national office or in a national campaign before 2022 and hadn't had the benefit of two years on the road due to lockdowns and border closures; what's more, he seemingly didn't see that he might not be match-fit when the time came. Until he did.

Murphy recalls a certain Albanese "ebullience" after the Eden-Monaro by-election in July 2020, and reports this brought a "constant assessment," or an "intervention," or something – whatever it was, it apparently took a conversation with the colleagues to bring things back to earth. That's changing; if there was any ebullience around in the second half of 2022, then it didn't take the colleagues to rein it in. Events kept this PM's feet pretty firmly on the ground.

I reckon Albo's "art of indeterminate age" – on the balcony at the Enmore Theatre and all that – might be another change coming. They all turn silver. When he runs for re-election, the PM will look at least sixty-two.

What else might change in coming years? He doesn't hate talking about himself, Anthony Albanese. The contrast between his happy warrior self-talk on his weight loss and Michelle Rowland's horror at the thought someone had been talking about her advice to him is very cute. The PM says "I" a fair bit when he's quoted in this essay. To be fair, he's being asked about himself. And Albanese's life circumstances – political, as much as personal – do mean he hasn't often been one to rely on a surrogate. Someone else to tell that funny story about his fridge never being empty of staples, or his credit card balance always being zero, or to introduce him by saying at least he never changed his footy team, rather than it being left to him to make the humblebrag himself. I wonder if that will change, whether the surrogates will find their voice, and how he'll help them find the space. I think it will, not least because we can already see the voices found and the spaces created by his colleagues in the governing project, and Murphy rightly zeroes in on this.

What we have in Canberra right now is a prime minister who is leading a real government-by-portfolio, as much as any in modern times. I think that tells us a lot about what comes next. If you're trying to answer the question, "How will this PM approach the big stuff: the Voice referendum, decision-making on the real economy, China?" then it seems to me the first thing you've got to do is rethink the question. You can't answer that question without also thinking about Linda Burney, about Jim Chalmers, about Penny Wong. That's a good thing.

Colleagues quoted on two key decisions of the Albanese Opposition – childcare and climate – rightly emphasise the big interventions the leader made, but it's equally clear these interventions weren't fundamentally about design. They were about purpose, political purpose as well as policy purpose. And they worked.

One other change. I watched at home with my eighteen-year-old son the first 7.30 interview Albanese gave after the 2019 election. The caucus had met that day and in the room Albo's candidacy had been unopposed. So there he is on television, saying, "Well, as the leader of the Labor Party" as his intro to every second answer, and junior turns to me and says, "Your man certainly does like being the 'leader of the Labor Party', doesn't he?" Penny Wong noticed this too, unsurprisingly. Her summary of the most important decision Anthony Albanese made between 2019 and 2022? "He decided to win, and he wanted to win the prime ministership, not the leadership of the Labor Party."

I just think that is so true.

The PM is not a new Albo; he's a bloke growing into a new job. But yes, in Katharine Murphy's essay we see an experienced politician changing – even more remarkable, we see a man aged over fifty *growing* – and the change that comes through most clearly is collegiality. The wolf runs with a pack.

What about a new politics? The Labor Party's national secretary and campaign director, Paul Erickson (another funny and serious character, whose post-election address to the National Press Club is worth printing out and popping inside this QE for future reference), is clearly sceptical. The election was won in the regions and the suburbs; one-off factors held down Labor's primary vote during the campaign.

Erickson also makes the very sound point that if we really must see in politics the exhausting trope that Labor infrequently wins from Opposition, the only general lesson of that is you can't draw any general lesson from that, because those wins are wildly discrete events, literally decades apart. He might have noted two other pertinent caveats to the "Labor winning from Opposition" trope. First, that's federal Labor. In state elections, the Labor Party has won from Opposition five times in the past nine years. Second, it really just means that "the Menzies government was long." Even in federal politics, Labor's last three governments went two terms, five terms and two terms. The federal Coalition's last three governments went three terms, four terms and three terms. Come on, guys.

Nevertheless, a big change did happen in 2022, when a key group of geographically concentrated Liberal voters switched, taking a heap of seats off the Coalition, making the path to majority for the LNP very hard, and hugely disrupting some entrenched habits and institutions in politics and the parliament.

To the extent that this emerges as sustained change, it may just be change back to a very old politics; when Murphy refers to "centre-right progressives," doesn't she just mean "liberals"? Hello, 1909. And hell yes, if liberalism and conservatism really are never, ever getting back together, that's great and amazing. In her biography of Alfred Deakin, the last liberal prime minister outside a conservative party, the historian Judith Brett observed:

> From the security of his cherished and comfortable childhood and the easy successes of his youth, Deakin never understood the grievance and injuries of working-class life, its humiliations and narcissistic wounds. The bitterness and pride which drove men like Billy Hughes or Andrew Fisher or Frank Anstey were a mystery to him …

Let's see if that's still a problem this time.

If it's not, and the liberals don't fuse into the conservative institutions again, does that mean a new politics? I dunno. What I do know is that the people who say it would mean there's a new politics also say the new politics is about three things, and one of them is *integrity*.

Which is where I come back to the question behind *Lone Wolf*. Not "What is Albo like?" but "How will Labor govern?" How will the prime minister lead? One more Murphy haiku:

> It would require the Labor Party not to devour itself and throw away government.
> "There's a plan," Albanese says. "There's always a plan."
> I can imagine the look of satisfaction that drifts across his face.

So can I. When the PM speaks about long-term governments, a lot of people hear lessons from 2007 to 2013, especially from 2010. Important lessons about process and progress — "big things done slowly and little things done quickly," in Treasurer Jim Chalmers' words. And very very obviously, yes, lessons about unity — the PM's overflow of emotion at the Lodge after the election when thanking colleagues for their teamwork as they had rallied in the campaign; tears of relief, Murphy thinks.

But I think more should be made of the likelihood that the PM has also learnt a lesson about trust. Yes, the ghost of 2010 says to work methodically, yes dear God obviously, it says don't eat your own, but I think the PM might hear it saying something else: you rarely build a long-term government by breaking election promises on tax.

And by the way, all that discussion of the NSW Left was really interesting. Meredith Burgmann's insights are particularly striking and I'd forgotten Andrew Leigh wrote that amazing paper. (Of course he did.) When the prime minister addressed the NSW Labor State Conference in the Sydney Town Hall last year, the first prime minister from New South Wales to do so this century, there was a little moment in the middle where he stopped, looked up and called out, "Delegate Albanese, Admin Committee!"

Very, very Albo (he may even have said "Albuh-neez"): funny, sentimental and something we probably won't hear at the conference this year. Things keep changing for the PM. That's the plan.

Michael Cooney

Nick Bryant

Often a new leader personifies a new politics, but that can hardly be said of Anthony Albanese. He is a Labor diehard at a time when the two major parties are in decline. He remains a pretty blokey pol at a time when politics is becoming more feminised. He is a cautious pragmatist on climate change when key constituencies in urban and corporate Australia are turning a deeper shade of green. He is a lifelong left-winger when the electorate clearly favours centrism. So Katharine Murphy's Quarterly Essay poses important questions about how Albanese is realigning himself with Australia's political realignment, and to what extent he pre-empted the new politics.

From the outset I should reveal that I consider myself one of Katharine's biggest fanboys. When I returned to Australia after eight years in America, she became one of the commentators I relied on to make sense of the fag end of the Morrison years and the quiet rise of Anthony Albanese. And sure enough, her essay is full of Murphisms, those enviably well-written lines and subtle observations that pepper her columns for *The Guardian*. Of Morrison's grubby attempt on election day to play the boat-people card, as a vessel carrying Sri Lankan refugees was intercepted in the Indian Ocean, she notes: "The final hours of desperate men were what they always are. Unworthy of the memoir." Her description of the formulation of Australian climate policy "as an exercise in swimming between the flags" is perfect, and could be applied more broadly. After spending time with Albanese at his home in Marrickville, she reveals that the prime minister never runs out of household staples – milk, frozen food, coffee, toilet paper, dog food for his beloved Toto – and has never paid a cent in interest on his credit cards. Albanese's backstory has been so heavily mined, not least by "Albo" himself, that any new biographical nuggets that make more sense of him are gratefully received – and these do help make more sense of him. Besides, in a polity that once obsessed over an empty fruit bowl, voters can presumably sleep easy at night knowing that the country is in the hands of a prime minister with a well-stocked freezer.

Katharine also avoids what could have been a pitfall of the Quarterly Essay format: to overthink a prime minister who does not overthink himself. Her subject is "a clever and patient strategist, with sharp political judgment," she notes, rather than a philosopher king. "Like his mentor Tom Uren, his political values are drawn from life, not philosophy or theory," she says. But neither does she underestimate him, an elephant trap that commentators have frequently plunged into, myself included.

What she offers is a frame to explain why he has become a more successful prime minister than many of us expected. This she puts down to his evolution "from lone wolf to collaborative actor," a process through which he came to rely more heavily on his talented team of ministers and tried to transcend the self-defeating factionalism of Labor politics.

Often in discussing the rise of Albo, the focus has been on what she calls the "front-end stuff." The dramatic weight loss. The switch to more fashionable eye-wear. But she is surely right to focus on what was happening behind the scenes, as Albanese sought to expand his circle beyond his two closest confidants, Penny Wong and Mark Butler, and mend fences with rival Labor factions.

Sure enough, one of the most admirable aspects of Albanese's prime ministership has been his willingness not only to delegate, but to encourage many of the star performers in his cabinet to shine. This feels more like an Albanese administration than an Albanese prime ministership. After decades of Australian politics becoming more presidential, he has made it more ministerial. In this age of narcissistic, performative politicians, he is showing us the value of an ensemble cast with multiple principal actors – a point of difference from Morrison, who evidently wanted to play many of the leading roles himself. Tellingly, one of the most eye-catching quotes in the essay comes not from the prime minister, but his treasurer. "My theory of governing," says Jim Chalmers, "is people will cop big things done slowly and little things done quickly, but not big things done quickly or little things done slowly." Even Bill Clinton or James Carville, who are renowned for their pithy rhetorical inversions, would struggle to put it better, although maybe we should think of this dictum more as a Keatingism, given that the treasurer's doctoral thesis was on the "brawler statesman."

Always there is the danger in writing this kind of essay of succumbing to an analytical form of reverse engineering, with plot mechanics neatly combining to produce a known outcome. Initially, I thought Katharine may be straying into this territory by highlighting as a pivotal moment Labor's new childcare policy, which became the centrepiece of Albanese's budget reply speech in October 2020. Back then, so much of the commentary focused on how the footy-loving "Albo" was a figure of reassurance to working-class male battlers, rather than to women, who often felt the burden of childcare. Covid also dominated the headlines. So was it really that much of a turning point?

Yet she presents a persuasive case. Childcare was a kitchen-table issue which the coronavirus brought into sharper relief, and also one which was usefully emblematic since it exposed the tone-deafness of the Morrison government. Albanese had opened up an important dialogue with women. As Georgie Dent, the executive director of The Parenthood, notes in the essay: "That childcare commitment was the first step towards winning office."

For all his smart political and policy choices, for all the times he has been the author of his own success, I still look upon Albanese as an extraordinarily lucky politician, a happy habit which does not lend itself to intellectualisation and which maybe receives short shrift in the essay. Albanese was elected, on the back of Labor's lowest primary since the 1930s, primarily because he was not Scott Morrison. One of the reasons he has enjoyed such a long political honeymoon is because Morrison continues to experience such a disastrous post-prime ministership. During the federal election, the teals prosecuted the case against the Morrison government often more effectively than he did. Even Albanese's brush with Covid, which forced him to spend a week in isolation, ended up being a boon. It allowed him to regroup when all those tedious gotcha questions were taking a toll, and brought his front-bench team of talents to the fore. His good fortune extends to the ALP having digested the lessons of the Rudd/Gillard/Rudd years, which has made it less cannibalistic (the caucus room, as well as its leader, has altered its dietary habits). And felicitous is the politician who faces across the dispatch box an Opposition leader with the negatives of a Peter Dutton.

Like all successful politicians, Albanese has made his own luck, and what he has achieved is in many ways exceptional. This veteran of Canberra politics has undertaken an extreme political and physical makeover, shedding policies as well as pounds, while at the same time safeguarding two of his prime assets: his honesty and authenticity. That is no mean feat.

In this new era, in this new politics, Albanese's skill as an intra-party peacemaker makes him ideally placed to serve as an inter-party coalition builder. So, too, as Katharine points out, does his experience of Julia Gillard's minority government, in which he served as Leader of the House. Needless to say, he wants Labor to become the natural party of government. But maybe he should set his sights instead on making the Liberals the natural party of Opposition. Certainly that possibility now presents itself, and he could achieve in Australia what has eluded progressive leaders in America or Britain, where there has long been a centre-left majority but also long stretches of conservative rule.

In the United States, the structural flaws of its democracy, which include the unrepresentativeness of the electoral college, the malapportionment of the Senate and gerrymandering of the House of Representatives, have prevented the Democrats from turning their numerical advantage among voters into an iron grip on presidential and congressional power. In Britain, the splintering of the progressive vote between Labour, the Liberal Democrats, the Greens and Scottish Nationalists has helped the Conservative Party dominate Westminster. But the appearance of the teal independents and the rise of the Australian Greens give Labor the chance to block the Liberals from returning to government for years to come. In this sense, Albanese does not need to personify the new politics. He just needs to make sure they continue to work in Labor's favour.

My take when I profiled Albanese for *The Monthly*, six months out from the federal election, pretty much mirrored the conventional wisdom of the time. I found him to be an adroit tactician with a compelling backstory; a likeable sort of bloke, if not a magnetic personality; a details man rather than a visionary; a mechanic rather than a Messiah. After the regicide of the coup years, and the regressive politics of Scott Morrison, he seemed well on his way to delivering on his promise of "renewal not revolution."

Back then, I dubbed him a repairman, but perhaps we should have looked upon Anthony Albanese as more of a restorer. As Katharine Murphy suggests in the superlative line of her essay, the new politics for him is the "[s]ame as the old politics, before the old politics lost its way."

Nick Bryant

Frank Bongiorno

In the week I'm writing this response to Katharine Murphy's admirable Quarterly Essay on the new politics, we've had two pointed reminders of the old. Scott Morrison appeared before the Robodebt royal commission, ducking and weaving as in days of yore, but with one major difference from those media conferences we came to abhor and avoid. In this forum, he was unable simply to avoid a question, patronise the questioner and then move on to another of his endless stream of deceptions.

Australians also heard from a woman, Sandra Bevan, who was a victim of this odious and unlawful system. A real battler — as distinct from the kind invented by John Howard to harvest votes — she was bullied, humiliated and cheated by a system designed to punish the poor and win the favour of voters and media hostile to welfare recipients. All in the land of the fair go.

In the same week, the attorney-general, Mark Dreyfus KC, announced that the government would be abolishing the Administrative Appeals Tribunal. As currently constituted, this body represents — as Dreyfus put it — a "disgraceful exhibition of cronyism." With its eighty-five former Liberal politicians, staffers, candidates and mates, it has become a high-end welfare system for Liberal Party people looking for their next "opportunity."

While the AAT is an especially notable example of the Coalition's way of running the country for the benefit of the well-connected — egregious not least because of its potential impact on the lives of so many Australians — it is just one among many of the country's institutions debauched during nine years of Coalition government. The old politics also saw the same kinds of people stuffed on to the boards of cultural institutions, even as several of those same institutions were so deprived of funding that some of them are now — quite literally — falling apart.

Is there a new politics? Murphy believes so, and I think she is right. For Murphy, it is about the decline of the two-party system and its ways. Unlike those parties' tendency towards what political scientists call the "electoral-professional model" – parties dominated by politicians and paid officials and with a thin rank-and-file base – the new politics is "bottom-up," arising from local communities. While it has a strong streak of pragmatism, it is also idealistic, and it elevates cooperation and conversation over the combat of partisan politics. It stresses integrity and transparency, in contrast with the old politics' pleasure in a backroom deal in a smoke-filled room or around a lazy Susan in a Sussex Street Chinese restaurant. It has in common with right-wing populisms an insurgent, disruptive quality, but it is supportive rather than corrosive of democratic norms and rational policy.

During the 2022 election, the teal "community independents" were the most "in your face" expression of the new politics, which is particularly attractive to younger people, the better educated, the professional and women. For decades, the major parties have seen the key to their future not among those they have – often pejoratively – treated as metropolitan elites, remote from the values and experiences of "real people" out in the suburbs and country towns. Western Sydney was seen as the testing ground for politics: as in Frank Sinatra's "New York, New York," if you could make it there, you could make it anywhere. Labor's most explicit experiment in this kind of politics occurred under Mark Latham, who expressed disdain for the "insiders" of the inner city and championed a politics of the suburbs. That ended poorly, and the 2007 Rudd election indicated that Labor's only real hope of electoral success lay in what Murphy calls a "big tent" approach that forms and then seeks to hold together an alliance of often diverse people and interests. But that ended badly too.

In the years since, Labor has never quite known which way to jump. There were champions of a politics that emphasised the need to connect with blue-collar workers with "traditional" and even "conservative" values. Some proponents of this view took inspiration from Blue Labour in the United Kingdom. Labor's defeat at the 2019 election – which some attributed to its loss of connection with traditional supporters in regional, Queensland and "coal" seats – boosted the idea that Labor needed to secure its blue-collar base, but proponents had little to say about how this approach might affect its standing with other kinds of voters. Its most vocal champion was Latham's old mate Joel Fitzgibbon. Murphy's account is revealing on how the party managed his internal criticism and eventually landed on a climate policy under Chris Bowen as minister that – in an evocative image from her essay – managed to swim between the flags.

There is a case that considering both Labor's climate policy and its commitments to childcare, it is unfair to characterise the party's approach at the 2022 election as small target. It was adventurous in its chasing of voters who wanted action on climate change, government integrity and equity for women, but who lived in electorates rarely inclined to throwing Liberals out of office. Jim Chalmers is quoted in the essay as suggesting it was a bigger program than Hawke's in 1983 and Rudd's in 2007. This is debatable, but it might not be wrong. What is less in doubt is that in 2022, metropolitan voters delivered a very clear message to any political parties or candidates inclined to ridicule or condemn their lifestyles, values or interests.

That brings us to Albanese. We have a good biography from Karen Middleton of a few years back, and Albanese has said plenty about his personal story on the public record. Nevertheless, I learnt more here. The overriding impression I had taken from his successful campaign was that he wished to be seen as a collaborative leader. The late political psychologist Graham Little would probably have seen in Albanese's style "group leadership," which he also attributed to Bob Hawke: "neighbourliness, translating the experience of life in smaller groups, like the family, into the nation as a whole." But Murphy suggests that Albanese has another side: a lone wolf quality that works as a tension with the more collegial approach. Albanese's stress on orderly government, his emphasis on process, his search for consensus, his ambition – also nurtured by Hawke – to turn Labor into the natural party of government: these suggest not only an identification with the Hawke era but a rejection – politely implicit, but still real enough – of the leadership style of Kevin Rudd. It is, of course, also a rejection of Morrison's outrageous breaches of Westminster conventions and practices that have a history stretching back centuries, such as his secret assumption of five ministries on top of the prime ministership.

Albanese seems to understand something that eluded Rudd. Rudd wanted to make his government the story each day, to win each 24-hour news cycle. That was great while the government's popularity lasted, not so great when things soured. Albanese realises that a sideshow featuring your opponents has its uses: we have an almost daily reminder of how bad the last government was, and therefore – until Peter Dutton and his colleagues make a more explicit break with their immediate past – what an alternative to an Albanese Labor government might yet look like.

Albanese also seems to have judged the present mood of electors well. They don't want partisan politics in their faces each and every day. They are over charismatic leadership. They are over silly stunts of the kind Morrison made his trademark. There is a dawning realisation that serious times and serious issues – the China relationship, climate change and energy policy, a fast-rising cost of living and unaffordable housing, a lack of integrity in government – call for a serious politics. The teal independents also benefited enormously from this impulse among many voters. The new government is well regarded because it has been practical and has restored a sense of order and civility to a politics that had been veering dangerously towards the right-wing populist model contemptuous of parliament, process and even policy.

One other Labor leader of Albanese's lifetime also seems to sit there as part of his make-up and project. That is Gough Whitlam. Albanese might once have been of the Hard Left – the kind of politics that was hardly enamoured of Whitlamite social democracy – but in his life story he is very much a product of the Whitlam era. As the son of a mother on a disability pension, living in public housing, he was the beneficiary of public support, as inadequate as that could sometimes be (and the stories Murphy tells of the experiences of his mother, Maryanne, in the health system are especially moving). He received a free university education, courtesy of Whitlam. He was mentored and employed by Whitlam government minister Tom Uren. Albanese's talk of a move towards universalism in childcare is as Whitlamite in its feel as his insistence that the Uluru Statement from the Heart and the Voice are definitive of his government's commitments, values and image, here and abroad.

Yet, as Murphy indicates, Albanese's government, like Whitlam's, finds itself in office at a time when the global economic situation is unconducive to the realisation of Labor ambition. The local fiscal situation will also pose challenges, not least while Labor remains committed to seeing through the stage three income tax cuts.

Still, like Whitlam, Albanese is not willing to die wondering, as Penny Wong told Murphy. We are in for an interesting ride.

Frank Bongiorno

Simon Jackman

Prime Minister Albanese, the victor, must sit centrestage in any account of the 2022 election. But as Murphy explores in her essay, Albanese is (or at least was) far less the agent of change driving a new politics than he was alternately a bystander and its beneficiary. Albanese's relevance to a new Australian politics is not in the context of the 2022 election per se. Rather, as Murphy notes towards the close of the essay, Albanese and the new politics cross paths through his tenure as prime minister, the policies a Labor government can enact and the politics of the next election.

We now know more about the "new politics" and the election than was available when Murphy penned her essay. Both major parties have conducted their reviews of the 2022 election and major academic studies of the electorate are now in the public domain.

Along with Ian McAllister (ANU), Sarah Cameron (Griffith) and Jill Sheppard (ANU), I was one of the principal investigators for the 2022 Australian Election Study (AES). The AES has surveyed a representative cross-section of the Australian electorate after every federal election since 1987, using consistently worded questions and methodology to examine what drives voter decision-making and how these factors change over time. AES data is therefore an authoritative source for assessing just what is "new" about the new politics and giving the 2022 election historical context.

Many analysts, Murphy among them, rightly emphasise the decline in major-party first-preference vote share, which is perhaps on the cusp of a critical threshold that will see minority government become commonplace in Canberra. The AES data supplies an important qualification to this observation. Because, at least for now, it is the Coalition that is suffering more from dealignment than Labor.

The AES shows that "new voters" are perhaps a bigger part of the story than a "new politics." Only about 1 in 4 voters under the age of forty report voting for the Coalition in 2022. The Coalition's vote share has fallen to parlous levels, not only among younger women and younger professionals, but right across the two youngest generations in the electorate, millennials and gen Z. At no time in the thirty-five-year history of the Australian Election Study have we observed such a low level of support for either major party in so large a segment of the electorate.

The reservoir of AES data accumulated over the last thirty-five years reveals "life cycle" effects in political loyalties; for instance, voters becoming more conservative as they age, a tendency we see almost everywhere around the democratic world. But the AES data shows these effects to be mild. Large, enduring or abrupt changes in levels of political support at the life course are unusual in Australian politics. Of more importance is the level of support for one side of politics over another from which a generation starts its political journey over the life course, something akin to a form of *generational imprinting*. Reactions to issues and a specific set of party leaders generate bumps and wiggles around a slight tendency towards conservatism over the life course. But the point from which a generation starts its political journey – the politics that defined its generation as it "comes of age" politically – is at least as important as any slow, mild maturation effects or transitory election-specific "shock."

These patterns provide important context for the decline in Coalition support observed in 2022. Millennials entered the electorate in the early 2000s, with about 35 per cent of this generation supporting the Coalition, a level which has now fallen to 25 per cent. Gen X first appear in the AES in 1987, with 40 per cent reporting support for the Coalition, with a slight trend away from this level in the thirty-five years since. Labor's vote has waned somewhat among Gen X, but this is almost entirely made up for in two-party preferred terms by Gen X's turn towards the Greens. If Australia does have a "new politics," one of its defining characteristics is that its "newest" voters skew heavily towards Labor and the Greens. This is a profound challenge for the Coalition, and literally a once-in-a-generation opportunity for Labor to cement its standing in this segment of the electorate over their life course, putting a distinct centre-left stamp on the "new politics."

Political scientists are often chided for the emphasis they attach to political institutions, constitutions, electoral laws and procedures, seemingly giving insufficient due to personalities and leaders in accounts of political, economic and social change. But one key institutional feature of Australian politics bears special mention in understanding why dealignment is not symmetric in its partisan consequences.

No political party likes to see its vote share go down. But preferential voting softens the blow for Labor. The current configuration of Australian politics means that Labor losing votes to the Greens usually costs Labor close to nothing – at least up until the point where they fall behind the Greens on first preferences or where tactical preference allocations among other parties and candidates could push the Greens ahead of Labor. In 2022, 86 per cent of Greens voters preferenced Labor ahead of the Coalition in House of Representatives elections; no other group preferenced Labor so strongly. In the smaller set of seats where we see preference flows between the Coalition parties, 90 per cent of Liberal preferences flowed to National Party candidates and 81 per cent vice versa. While not coalition partners, Greens preference flows to Labor are as strong as those between the capital "C" Coalition partners, the difference being the Greens won 12 per cent of the vote and ran candidates in all 151 House of Representatives seats.

Further, keep in mind that no successful teal challenger was a majority winner or even a plurality winner on first preferences. Zali Steggall was an incumbent in 2022 and was the first-preference plurality winner with 45 per cent; Steggall also outpolled Tony Abbott in 2019. But for the six successful teal challengers, none won the most first-preference votes and two won with less than 30 per cent of first preferences. If these had been decided on "first-past-the-post," a lot more Coalition voters would have needed to defect and very different campaign strategies would have been implemented by both incumbents and challengers.

Institutions matter. And in Australian politics, preferential voting is helping Labor moderate the effects of dealignment and was critical to unseating six "heartland" Liberal incumbents.

Murphy repeatedly quotes Labor's national secretary, Paul Erikson, on the key role of Morrison's unpopularity in shaping the outcome of the 2022 election. AES data allows us to add some vivid historical context to Erikson's conclusion. Since the 1990 election, the AES has been asking survey respondents to rate major-party leaders on a ten-point "strongly dislike" to "strongly like" scale. By the 2022 election, Morrison was not just unpopular, but historically unpopular, his average rating of 3.8 on the ten-point scale making him the least-popular PM or Opposition leader ever seen in AES data. Barnaby Joyce fared even worse, scoring 3.2.

Albanese's average rating was 5.3, placing him in the middle of the pack, the eighth-most popular election winner out of thirteen spanned by the AES data. In 2019, Morrison's average rating was 5.1 against Bill Shorten's 4.0. The 1.3 point fall in Morrison's average rating from 2019 to 2022 pushed Morrison not only into historically unprecedented unpopularity for an incumbent PM, but with a pace unseen in any of the other election-to-election, leader-specific comparisons available in the AES data.

It is difficult to test for causation in "one shot" public-opinion surveys. The adage that warns against conflating correlation and causation is the political scientist's touchstone. Moreover, asking voters as to whether they vote "on the issues" or for or against the party leaders almost surely produces an overestimate of issue voting: many survey respondents lean towards a socially desirable presentation of themselves as substantive issue-based voters before nominating party loyalty or assessments of the leaders. With those caveats, 53 per cent of 2022 AES respondents said their vote was driven by policy differences, down from 66 per cent in 2019. Leadership qualities had more "leverage" on the vote in 2022 than in 2019.

All this is to say that, yes, 2022 was a remarkable election for all the reasons Murphy recounts: the major-party primary vote for House of Representatives candidates reached new lows; Labor has formed government with less than a third of first-preference votes; conservative forces have their lowest share of House seats since World War II, losing hitherto "heartland" seats; and Climate 200 and community-supported independents introduced a novel form of political organisation and campaigning to Australian politics. We need to add to the list an incumbent prime minister who had lost and was losing the respect and approval of the electorate at a spectacular rate, whose last-ditch attempt at explaining away his governing style ("bulldozer") was paired with the image of him knocking a small child to the ground on a soccer pitch during a campaign stunt in the closing days of the campaign.

Macroeconomic management, climate change and energy policy, industrial relations, the national integrity commission and the Voice to Parliament is the substantive terrain over which the parties will compete for votes in 2025. With Morrison in the rear-view mirror by the next election, Albanese's and Labor's performance on these issues will determine whether it capitalises on the historic opportunity before it, imprinting loyalty to Labor on gen Z and millennials over the course of their lives.

Simon Jackman

Carol Johnson

Professor James Walter has described Katharine Murphy as "one of our most astute political observers" when it comes to analysing the personas and performances of our political leaders. *Lone Wolf* draws a masterly portrait of the attributes that facilitated Anthony Albanese becoming prime minister and that may assist in his managing of the "new politics" as major-party support declines. In the process, Murphy provides an insightful analysis not just of a developing political persona but of a changing political landscape. Murphy characterises the "clean and green" new politics as eschewing "major-party custom and practice," being "bottom-up rather than top-down," idealistic and aspirational while championing dialogue, positivity, integrity and transparency over division. She suggests that Albanese will draw on the lessons he learnt during the Gillard period to manage relations with key independents who represent the new politics. Doing so will facilitate their ongoing challenge to the Liberal Party, even though he doesn't need the independents' support in the House of Representatives. (Albanese has required the support of independent senator David Pocock in the Senate.) However, there are some issues raised by Murphy's analysis that are worth considering further. Labor's task is complicated by the fact that it is having to negotiate the new politics at the same time as it negotiates some very old political issues. Traditional social cleavages and antagonisms remain and will complicate Labor's strategies, despite Albanese's claims that he will bring Australians together.

For example, Murphy cites Albanese's proud assertion that Labor represents "the interests of the vast majority of Australians," including being able to "work with business and unions." Yet Labor still needs to address the traditional social democratic issue of how to reduce inequality under capitalism, while managing the relationship between business and labour in the process. As I explain in my book *Social Democracy and the Crisis of Equality*, economic inequality has increased in recent years, partly due to neoliberal policies that have contributed to wage stagnation and a decline in real wages. The pandemic has exacerbated economic inequality even further. Albanese has often evoked former Labor PM Bob Hawke's consensus politics to suggest that an Albanese government will bring both business and unions together to improve workers' standards of living. However, Hawke's rapprochement was based on an Accord process that facilitated business reducing its wages bill, while workers were supposedly compensated by an increased "social wage" expenditure on health, welfare and education. By contrast, the Albanese government aims to increase real wages in the longer term, rather than restrain – or even cut – them, as Hawke and Keating did.

The Albanese government's task will be made even harder by major inflationary pressures and an uncertain international economy. Furthermore, Labor's ability to increase compensatory government expenditure, including welfare spending, is constrained by the need to manage a large deficit. That deficit will be further affected by revenue losses due to the planned stage three tax cuts. Given these dilemmas, we have already seen the government delay the full implementation of wage rises for aged-care workers, despite Labor having made a strong case for such wage rises. The government has succeeded in passing industrial relations legislation through parliament that it hopes will facilitate wage rises. However, it has done so in the face of considerable business opposition and only after making concessions to David Pocock. Pocock had been particularly concerned about the implications for small business (as indeed had some teal independents in the House of Representatives). There are also doubts that the measures included, such as multi-employer bargaining, will be sufficient to ensure adequate wage rises in the current economic climate, especially given business resistance.

Many of the new politics independents have a small "l" liberal background that is sympathetic to business, so Labor may encounter ongoing challenges in managing parliamentary relations with them. Outside of parliament, business opposition can result in well-funded campaigns against Labor and a resulting perception that Labor governments are poor economic managers. Voters employed in the private sector can be particularly worried about the prospect of reduced private-sector investment and job losses. Business campaigns against Labor governments have contributed to the electoral defeats of the Chifley, Whitlam, Keating and Rudd governments. Murphy cites Albanese's concern that Labor's poor relationship with business during the 2019 election campaign had contributed to Bill Shorten's defeat.

Climate change policy is another area where relationships with at least some sections of business are still problematic for Labor. Murphy states that Labor's Minister for Climate Change, Chris Bowen, has been "attracted to the idea of framing climate action as the unfinished element of the economic reforms Labor had pursued since the early 1980s." Yet this is not a new framing; it is one that Penny Wong used when she was climate change minister in Kevin Rudd's first government. Unfortunately, Wong was only successful in convincing some sections of business that Labor's climate change reforms were necessary, with the Rudd government facing considerable opposition from the large polluters.

Labor has managed to pass its reduced emissions target through parliament with support from the Greens and independents. However, we wait to see how successful the party will be in introducing further measures, including its attempts to tweak the existing safeguard mechanism to reduce emissions by big polluters. Fortunately for Albanese, much of Labor's safeguard mechanism policy can be implemented via regulation, thereby bypassing parliament and the need for either Greens or Coalition support in the Senate. However, a key aspect − namely the stockpiling and trading of carbon credits by overachieving firms to under-achieving ones − would need to be passed by legislation. It is a measure designed to placate those businesses that will not sufficiently reduce their carbon pollution, while rewarding those that will overachieve. As with proposed carbon trading during the Rudd era, Labor is facing difficulty obtaining Greens support, given that the Greens see Labor's cautious measures as facilitating big emitters. Meanwhile, the Coalition is resorting to old political strategies, with its Opposition energy and climate spokesman, Ted O'Brien, denouncing Labor's climate change measures as a "carbon tax."

Climate change is not the only field where Labor faces old arguments and culture-war issues. Murphy also cites Albanese's statement that Labor respects "First Nations people" as part of his argument that Labor represents "the interests of the vast majority of Australians." Yet that "embrace" of broader forms of equality also comes with longstanding political divisions. Not only have the Nationals opposed the Voice, but Peter Dutton has repeatedly raised questions regarding the form the Voice will take. Meanwhile, radical critics, such as Senator Lidia Thorpe, have questioned the Voice from the left, raising concerns about how effective it will be and its implications for black sovereignty.

As with climate change and the republic, Labor must solve the dilemma that addressing the conservative issues raised by the Liberals risks alienating more progressive supporters. Murphy rightly notes Albanese's emotional intelligence, but it might not be a match for a culture war–style fear campaign from the right coupled with feelings of disappointment and negativity from the left. After all, Rudd's Carbon Pollution Reduction Scheme failed to get through parliament when the Greens joined the Liberals to vote against it. The republic referendum failed when the votes of conservative opponents to a republic were bolstered by the "no" votes of progressives who supported a republic but not the specific model proposed. Peter Dutton may lack the dexterous footwork of an Albanese, who likes to keep his opponents "dancing," but Dutton is not without room to manoeuvre. As Murphy reminds us, the new politics can also take an anti-progressive form. Trump is an example of new politics — "a classic disruptor." Dutton has well-established cultural warrior credentials on which to draw, which owe as much to John Howard as to the former American president.

Clearly, Albanese will be hoping that Peter Dutton proves to be out of step with the new politics rather than an alternative manifestation of it. Albanese will try to utilise the new politics' emphasis on "dialogue over combat" to pursue a successful parliamentary agenda. He'll be hoping that the new independents' preference for making some progress rather than none, along with the Greens' apparent greater willingness to compromise, continue to gel with social democracy's traditional pursuit of incremental reform. Nonetheless, as Murphy acknowledges, the Greens will continue to target Labor seats and future teal-style independents may do so too. Negotiating old battles while managing the new politics will not be easy. So far Labor has enjoyed significant legislative success. However, "swimming between the flags," as Murphy argues Labor has successfully done, may yet prove to be a far more difficult exercise in government than it was in Opposition.

Carol Johnson

LONE
WOLF

Correspondence

Luca Belgiorno-Nettis

The subtitle of Katharine Murphy's *Lone Wolf* – "Albanese and the new politics" –
is a tease. "New" works every time: new toothpaste, new art, new idea. There was
little that was particularly new in the political campaigning of 2022 – except what
catapulted six freshly minted teal candidates into heartland Liberal seats. The question is: what was it? Something transformative seems to be emerging.

No doubt the success of the teals – and the Greens – was enhanced by having
a cartoonish, coal-carrying villain named Scott Morrison and by the Coalition's
lack of a raison d'être, other than keeping the other side out of office. It was amazing to witness the unprecedented levels of grassroots support. In Monique Ryan's
seat of Kooyong, for example, there were over 1500 volunteers – a frankly astound-
ing number. The public's desire to be involved in the campaigning – active in teal
seats, but absent in the major party branches – is a message to the big-tent parties.

The appearance of independents in parliament is nothing new, but it was the
"people-powered model of community organising" that was unconventional. Pioneered by Cathy McGowan in the seat of Indi in Victoria, then followed up by Zali
Steggall and Kerryn Phelps in New South Wales, they all unseated long-standing
incumbents, including – famously, in Steggall's case – Tony Abbott. Murphy is
keen to understand how Albanese can possibly "[push] against the mega-trend of
major-party depletion" and "the lowest primary vote ever for an incoming government." For Albanese, it begins with a comprehensive policy agenda and, to be
fair, his government delivered beyond expectations in the last sitting weeks of
2022. That's a great start, but a government prosecuting an agenda may not suffice.
That's old politics, done better. Albanese himself admits, "People have been very
frustrated with the political system and process, and why wouldn't they be?"

Murphy describes campaigns as "message wars mediated by an incurious, dead-
ening apparatus intent on seeking heat, not light," and representative democracy
as "a spectacle of pulverising, naysaying partisan politics." With politics being so

pugnacious, there's an obvious appeal in having a fresh batch of independents, especially when each comes untainted by a lifetime of trench warfare. Zoe Daniel says, reflecting on the major parties, "It must feel quite unnatural for them, to try and take point-scoring out of it, to try and look at it as having productive conversations and collaborate." In Perth's electorate of Curtin, Kate Chaney declares that she's "doing politics differently."

In this election, climate change was always going to be the hot topic. "Swimming Between the Flags" is Murphy's title for her chapter on the ALP's policy work behind the 43 per cent emissions reduction goal: the safe place where Labor's constituency could feel comfortable swimming. The Albanese government has now enacted the target, with Greens' support – unlike the fiasco in 2009 – with Adam Bandt trumpeting that this parliament could be "a great era of progressive reform," and that "one of the lessons from the climate negotiations is the only limit on more progressive action is Labor's ambition." After more than a decade of climate wars, the political rhetoric remains eerily the same.

Murphy also unpicks Climate 200's contribution to the election. Eighteen months out, Simon Holmes à Court, its founder, started putting together a team and engaged Kos Samaras, "a long-time Labor operative who was now running ... campaigns for the Melbourne-based lobbying firm RedBridge." Samaras's advice was that Liberal electorates with "high numbers of young professional women" and a growing "renter cohort" could be swung over. "All we needed to do," Samaras tells Murphy, "was build a particular brand of politics that was going to ... meet these needs that people had, that [was] sort of centrist, socially progressive, on climate very progressive, with a bit of pragmatism." Climate 200 helped strategise and fund each of the teals' campaigns: get the messaging right, build the brand and target the spend. Again, old politics done well.

New politics would suggest more – new politics addresses the loss of agency and the disaffection that many have with the "naysaying spectacle." Australians aren't alone in this. In 2020, the OECD published "Catching the Deliberative Wave," a review across member states, highlighting how trust in democracy is waning around the globe, and, on the flip side, the transformation happening in citizen engagement. The presidents of Ireland, France and Germany have now all implemented citizens' assemblies.

For those unfamiliar with the concept, these assemblies are a public judgment mechanism akin to a criminal jury, and thus the opposite of a public opinion tool. Selected by civic lottery, the participants are exposed to a diversity of expert information and sources, including many of their own choosing, and given time to question and discuss. With the incentive of being listened to and getting a response from the government, citizens work diligently to make common-ground recommendations.

Albanese, with an eye on a second term, says, "I'll be standing [in 2025] and saying we had this agenda: action on climate, economic growth, new industry, skills, aged care, cheaper childcare, cheaper medicines, advancing gender equality, Voice to Parliament. This is a significant agenda, and Australia needs stable government going forward ... You need a government to get things done."

All true, and it's heartening to see that, in early December, the agenda might now include structural reform. The Minister for Home Affairs, Clare O'Neil, announced the establishment of a "Strengthening Democracy Taskforce"; and the Assistant Minister for the Republic, Matt Thistlethwaite, is exploring the use of citizens' assemblies for the proposed republic referendum. Allegra Spender, the teal in Wentworth, has also just called for a citizens' assembly "to consider how best to fund elections." These latest initiatives seem to be building on the public's hankering to do politics differently. In Spender's words, "If we did this, we could get an answer that puts the Australian people first, not parties, politicians or vested interests." This appears to be the new current lifting the wave of community independents.

Luca Belgiorno-Nettis

Rachel Nolan

In *Lone Wolf*, Katharine Murphy offers an explanation for a fascinating yet little-remarked feature of recent Australian politics: the physical and apparently temperamental transformation of the prime minister before our very eyes. Out is the "insurgent," "bomb-throwing" Albo, a character so compelling that Lech Blaine argued it was the model Scott Morrison plagiarised to invent ScoMo. In is a quiet, thoughtful character who, in round glasses and felt hat, looks for all the world like John Curtin during the war.

Murphy's explanation is that far from being "Queer Eye'd" in pursuit of ambition, Albanese is an outsider who's moved in, bringing a considered and collaborative approach to leadership in disrupted times.

Albanese's goals, Murphy writes, are to make Labor the natural party of government and to deliver meaningful change. His fascinations in order of preference are "power, politics, parliament, policy and process."

Murphy's analysis is satisfying. The bigger question is: can he succeed?

After the devastation of the 2019 election, Labor adopted a more modest program, promising an expansion of public services through cheaper childcare, greater access to Medicare and more investment in the NDIS, as well as some harder-to-deliver programs, such as a 43 per cent emissions reduction target, greater investment and efficacy in Australia's defence posture and an end to relentless, often partisan attacks on public services and the welfare state. With progressive politics having spent a generation in retreat and trust in politics at historic lows, even this agenda may be hard to get up.

Labor's approach is a unique political experiment. In abandoning the model of an "all politics, all the time" front man dominating the debate, Albanese differs not just from Scott Morrison, but from every post-war Labor prime minister except Julia Gillard.

In ditching pizzazz for policy and process, the government is choosing two of its leader's lesser preoccupations. It's a radically conventional approach at a time when the weakening and politicisation of the public service has become common-place and democratic institutions are threatened globally by nationalists and a raging hard right.

Less than a year in, the Albanese government has begun to define its approach. There is a proper cabinet process, complete with functioning committees. Ministerial staffer roles were publicly advertised and there are six new public service heads. First among them, Glyn Davis – an exceptional public servant and thinker who has led both the Queensland premier's department and the University of Melbourne – has replaced Morrison's former chief of staff Phil Gaetjens as head of the prime minister's department.

Legislation for an integrity commission has been introduced and an expensive decision made to abolish rather than "square up" the irredeemable Administrative Appeals Tribunal.

While these are sound high-profile decisions, the success of the government's approach will depend on the far less sexy work of improving capability and integrity at the heart of the Australian public service (APS). In the past twelve months, a series of public inquiries at both state and Commonwealth levels has revealed deep flaws in public service integrity. Queensland's Coaldrake review, the Barilaro inquiry in New South Wales and a string of Commonwealth audits, royal commissions and reviews have heard shameful evidence of senior public servants taking it upon themselves to suppress bad news because they have sensed, or been told directly by out-of-line political staffers, that uncomfortable advice will not be smiled upon.

This dynamic – in which public servants become avatars of their political masters, and politicians lack access to frank and fearless advice – is risky for everyone. Timid public servants leave themselves open to carrying the can for what should be political decisions, but there's also the risk that governments, lacking the rigour of good policy advice, get it wrong.

Political decision-making is an art form; a magic concoction of ideology, evidence, power dynamics and a nuanced understanding of public opinion. It's best undertaken by politicians who, unlike public servants, are masters of the discipline.

Fixing this will take serious reform and time. So far, the new government's approach relies largely on the recommendations of the Thodey report, a review into the APS commissioned by Malcolm Turnbull in 2018 and largely shelved by Scott Morrison. The review began with a concerning starting point, identifying that just 30 per cent of Australians trusted public services, that the public sector spent 12 per cent more than the private sector in running old digital platforms and that the APS was excessively atomised across agencies.

While Morrison rejected any suggestion that the APS would take a leadership role in policy development, the new government – under public service minister Katy Gallagher – has set about an extensive overhaul of the APS, with ongoing capability reviews, better organisational and industrial coordination, the pursuit of diversity including First Nations employment, the development of an in-house consulting model and a commitment to measure and report on public service efficiency and trust.

The government has appointed Gordon de Brouwer, a former secretary of the environment department, on a two-year contract to lead the reform. In a significant move, it has also begun publishing communiqués from meetings of the departmental Secretaries Board.

The reforms are sound and represent normalisation rather than a step change. There's no trendy, new democracy–style launch into citizen's juries, no regionalisation of service delivery – as Kevin Rudd pioneered and Barnaby Joyce ham-fistedly applied – and no money for wholesale investment in digital service delivery as has occurred in New South Wales.

But getting to the sweet spot of the relationship between the public service and the executive will take some doing and, if successful, will test the integrity of the government in a system now so used to ministers just getting their way with a disregard for process or policy.

Far from being an exercise in giving the APS what it wants, the reforms will need to reflect an understanding that an elected government does have a mandate but that the APS can and should know deeply what it's talking about. With the trickiest conversations inevitably happening behind closed doors, we will have to wait for the entrails of the first conflicts to be revealed either in key departures or gripping Senate Estimates hearings.

In the last Oxford University survey, Australia's public service was rated the fifth-best in the world, which might come as a surprise to anyone who's watched the recent Commonwealth inquiries or tried to deal with Centrelink. The service might be fine by international standards, but there is an ocean of improvement to be made in culture, diversity (including an ability to imagine life beyond Canberra), digital capability, integrity and excellence.

There is no higher calling than public service – for our political and bureaucratic actors alike. We will know all of this is getting somewhere when Australian universities, many of which have abandoned teaching public administration, return to the field and produce graduates who rush not to intern with the World

Bank in Washington, but in Treasury, the Department of Prime Minister and Cabinet and the climate change department. These are the places where the real action is happening.

Achieving such a change may at times be uncomfortable for a prime minister and cabinet already nearly one year into a three-year term, but if the goal is to make the Labor project sustainable, then the best-quality advice will immeasurably benefit the cause. Australia has long provided a leading example to the world in our democratic institutions. Compulsory voting provides ballast to our democracy; our health, education and welfare systems are world-leading, and we famously took a lead role in the establishment of the United Nations.

If Australia can succeed in de-politicising and strengthening its public service at this critical moment in history, it will again be an exemplar for the English-speaking world to follow. If it doesn't, it's hard to say where we go. There is no plan B on the horizon.

Rachel Nolan

Katharine Murphy

Christopher Pyne, a lifelong major-party partisan, is clearly a new politics sceptic, but when it comes to Anthony Albanese, he sees the same political protagonist I see. We've both engaged in Albo-ology, watching the prime minister from different vantage points for a couple of decades, and have evidently reached substantially similar conclusions about who this man is and how he operates.

There is reassurance in this. To borrow the *Hamilton* jingle, journalists are never in the room where it happens. We press-gallery types are close, ecosystem-adjacent, but there are boundaries we can't cross. I am always acutely conscious that politicians (borrowing this time from T.S. Eliot) prepare a face to meet the faces that they meet. I'm never entirely certain that I have the measure of the person. Pyne has been in rooms with Albanese, bantering and bartering, in many different political contexts, high stakes and low – places I will never see. I'm glad there are no significant divergences in our impressions. Pyne's is a generous response. All these responses are. I'm grateful for the positive reception, because these Quarterly Essays are magnificent projects, but they are beasts that plunge writers even further into self-doubt. It's very hard to get them right, both in tone and in substance, and the topics I have attempted aren't static.

My favourite observation from Pyne – one I wished I'd located in the mist in my head – was a racing analogy to capture Albanese's long-held desire to be in the centre of things, but always slightly off-camera. Pyne notes as that as Albanese rose through the viper pit of professional politics, he "kept his rivals in front of him, where he could see them. In racing terms he was one back, on the outside." It's a good line, because it encapsulates a modus operandi that has survived the transition from aspirant to holder of the office. In the opening months of his prime ministership, Albanese has prioritised a mode of operation that feels measurably different after a run of regicidal presidential operators in Canberra. As the ever-perspicacious Nick Bryant notes, in an age of narcissistic performative politicians, Albanese has opened his prime ministership by showing Australians "the value of an ensemble cast with multiple principal actors – a point of difference from Morrison, who evidently wanted to play many of the leading roles himself."

Will Albanese's return to first among equals work? Will it all end in tears? Possibly. This is the Labor Party. That has certainly been known to happen. But for now, Australians have experienced a circuit-breaker. Politics is a permanent campaign, but we've seen plenty of governing since May 2022. The government has sped into office like it's five minutes to midnight, but the public-facing operation is tranquil. For the first time in more than a decade, government has been about something more than crises and coups, even if the program is more cautiously pragmatic (to borrow from Nick again) than many progressives might like.

Michael Cooney also makes a cut-through observation on the theme of ensembles, but before I get there, full disclosure. I am close to 100 per cent confident that I borrowed Albanese being an old dog for a hard road from him, so it's decent of him to praise me for lifting his thought without serving a copyright infringement notice. Also, that friend he texted was me. Just for the record. But to his cut-through observation. Cooney notes our current prime minster deploys the vertical pronoun frequently "because he doesn't hate talking about himself." During his professional life as an adviser and wordsmith for Labor leaders, Cooney kicked around in proximity to Albanese for years, so we both know this is true. But we both also know this tendency or habit has been *necessary* for the reformed Lone Wolf in the Lodge. Albanese is a factional powerbroker, so he has legions of acolytes. Lots of people owe him, and he's one of the most networked politicians I've ever seen. But his inner inner sanctum used to be small. Albanese has also maintained an unusual degree of control for a person in public life for the best part of three decades over the basics of his life story, including deciding when he will share key details, like finding his Italian father after his mother's death (detailed in Karen Middleton's excellent biography; if you haven't read that yet, do).

When I set out to write this essay, I imposed a rule with the many people I interviewed. We could certainly chat on background (if you aren't fluent in the conventions of journalism, this means any information shared in the conversation is usable without attribution). But I would not be using any blind quotes in this essay, or "sources said." This kind of reporting is necessary sometimes; people can't always own newsworthy information for valid reasons. But the convention is overused, and it's sometimes just plain corrosive. For this profile, colleagues would need to talk about the prime minister (then at the peak of his power) honestly and on the record. I wanted candour, for posterity. Seeking this might sound like no big deal, but in the world of politics, direct reflections on the leader can be fraught. Because it's fraught, people often overthink what they will say, and there was a bit of that evident in this exercise. But fortunately, most didn't overthink in the end, and I was grateful for the degree of frankness in many of the observations.

This context about my methodology for this Quarterly Essay sets up Cooney's point. He notes that until now, Albanese has had primary carriage of his own story because his life circumstances – "political, as much as personal – do mean he hasn't often been one to rely on a surrogate. Someone else to tell that funny story about his fridge never being empty of staples, or his credit card balance always being zero, or to introduce him by saying at least he never changed his footy team, rather than it being left to him to make the humblebrag himself." Cooney wonders whether that will change. It's the right question, and one I set out to test. Albanese, as the thirty-first prime minister of Australia, can't control his own narrative anymore. People don't care much about Opposition leaders, but the story of a prime ministership is the story of a country. It's common property. Leaders belong to the people and the history of this time will be told by multitudes – journalists in the first draft, and proper historians, of course (I'm looking forward to an updated edition of *Dreamers and Schemers*, Frank Bongiorno!) – as well as colleagues, friends, foes, rivals, successors.

Knowing the essay would very likely be the first long-form profile-style reportage of his prime ministership, I wanted to capture two things: a first-hand account from Albanese about how he operates and why he behaves in certain ways; and the collective voice of a new government as it transitioned to power. I wanted to test and record the impressions of the surrogates (as Cooney puts it) because a key narrative arc in the essay is Albanese consenting to be part of a collective "governing project" (Cooney's locution again) after a professional lifetime of minority group in minority faction insurgency. I witness these transitions from my second-floor office in Parliament House, and feel it's my job to capture them. The overarching aim of my first Quarterly Essay – *The End of Certainty: Scott Morrison and Pandemic Politics* – was to capture not only the essential facts but also the mood of the first six months of 2020, those visceral months of "lives and livelihoods." This was an incredible time: journalists masked up, rattling around in a near-empty Parliament House with a group of leaders having to work out hour by hour how best to stop people dying of coronavirus before we had vaccines – a time I knew we would all forget, or radically reinterpret, the further we got away from it.

The Morrison essay was a study in two parts, a man in a moment, and so is the latest one. *Lone Wolf* is the story of how Albanese rose to lead the Labor Party, and then surfed to office on, in part, a teal wave. Pyne is a new politics sceptic. Historian

Bongiorno, in his response – not so much. The facts tell us new politics is, actually, a thing. If we look at the run of federal elections over decades, the hard data plots a major-party system in decline. The decline of mass political movements has left both the major parties vulnerable to base shrinkage, a phenomenon that feeds narrowcasting politics. As major parties become more bespoke and less representative, pandering to the prejudices of their shrinking bases, the electoral splintering intensifies. The relevant case study in 2022 illustrating this rusting-off phenomenon was the Coalition's decade-long obduracy on climate change driving a collapse in support among metropolitan centre-right progressives – small "l" liberals.

We are witnessing an electoral realignment. This isn't moot. But it's a moving phenomenon. The next manifestation of the long-term trend is hard to predict. What can be known now is that the new bottom-up community-based movements, as Bongiorno says, favour "integrity and transparency, in contrast with the old politics' pleasure in a backroom deal in a smoke-filled room or around a lazy Susan in a Sussex Street Chinese restaurant." This movement "has in common with right-wing populisms an insurgent, disruptive quality, but it is supportive rather than corrosive of democratic norms and rational policy." He sees another element to the new politics: the return of seriousness to meet the seriousness of the times. The teals tapped this mood, and so did Albanese, Bongiorno says. "The new government is well regarded because it has been practical and has restored a sense of order and civility to a politics that had been veering dangerously towards the right-wing populist model contemptuous of parliament, process and even policy."

Rachel Nolan takes us to the nub of the thing. Albanese wants to "make Labor the natural party of government and to deliver meaningful change." Albanese is perfectly comfortable in this disrupted electoral world, but he wants to shape it by renewing the case for major-party politics. Nolan then poses a question none of us can answer: "can he succeed?"

Who knows? That's the story of the next parliamentary term.

Thank you again for all of the responses – truly above and beyond. I am certain all the contributors would have preferred to enjoy their first real holiday in three years without parsing *Lone Wolf*. The reader response has also been amazing, and I'm grateful. Thanks most of all to Chris Feik and his editorial team for being a dream to work with. Thank you to Lenore Taylor and my Canberra colleagues for facilitating some writing time, and thank you to David Marr, a mentor in all the important ways. Love and gratitude to my husband – partner in life, thinking, writing, striving.

Katharine Murphy

Postscript: I received one important correction to the essay after publication, from Dr David Champion, who wrote: "While it was momentarily tempting to leave uncorrected the kind tribute to me about the medical care of [Anthony Albanese's] mother Maryanne as both rheumatologist and surgeon, I cannot do so. It was a long time ago and, with all Mr Albanese has had on his mind over many years, it seems that he has merged the memory of David Champion as rheumatologist and Dr Frank Robertson, highly skilful orthopaedic surgeon who performed the surgery on her hands and feet, into the one person (me).

"It had been a great privilege to have been involved in Maryanne's medical care and I would like to think that this was a good example of rheumatologist and orthopaedic surgeon working in such a harmonious relationship that we appeared to be one person in hazy memory.

"Young Anthony was an inspiringly good son from my perspective."

Luca Belgiorno-Nettis is the founder and director of The newDemocracy Foundation and the co-author of *The A, B and C of Democracy*.

Frank Bongiorno is a professor of history at the Australian National University and a distinguished fellow of the Whitlam Institute at Western Sydney University. He is most recently the author of *Dreamers and Schemers: A Political History of Australia*.

Nick Bryant recently returned to Australia after serving as one of the BBC's most senior foreign correspondents. He is the author of *When America Stopped Being Great* and *The Rise and Fall of Australia*. He is a senior fellow at the Sydney Policy Lab at Sydney University.

Michael Cooney is general manager of public affairs for Maurice Blackburn Lawyers. He was speechwriter to Prime Minister Julia Gillard and documented Labor's government from 2010 to 2013 in his book *The Gillard Project*. Michael has also served as principal policy adviser to federal Labor leaders and was founding policy director at the progressive think-tank Per Capita.

Saul Griffith is an engineer and inventor. He has been principal investigator on research projects for NASA, Advanced Research Projects Agency–Energy, the National Science Foundation and US Special Operations Command. He was awarded the MacArthur "Genius Grant" in 2007. He is a founder of the organisations Rewiring America and Rewiring Australia, and the author of *Electrify* and *The Big Switch: Australia's Electric Future*.

Simon Jackman was professor of political science and statistics at Stanford University between 1997 and 2016, and from 2016 to 2022 was CEO of the US Studies Centre at the University of Sydney. In 2022 Jackman was one of the principal investigators of the Australian Election Study.

Carol Johnson is an emerita professor of politics at the University of Adelaide. Her most recent book is *Social Democracy and the Crisis of Equality: Australian Social Democracy in a Changing World*.

Katharine Murphy has worked in Canberra's parliamentary press gallery since 1996 for the *Australian Financial Review*, *The Australian* and *The Age*, before joining *Guardian Australia*, where she is the political editor. She won the Paul Lyneham Award for Excellence in Press Gallery Journalism in 2008 and has been a Walkley Award finalist twice. She is a director of the National Press Club and the author of *On Disruption* and Quarterly Essays *The End of Certainty* and *Lone Wolf*.

Rachel Nolan is special adviser at Deloitte Access Economics, chair of public policy think-tank The McKell Institute Queensland, and a regular lecturer in public governance and finance at University of Queensland International Development. She is a former Queensland government minister, including for transport and finance.

Christopher Pyne was a minister in the Howard, Abbott, Turnbull and Morrison governments, serving finally as Minister for Defence and Leader of the House before retiring in 2019 after twenty-six years in the Australian House of Representatives. He now is head of Pyne and Partners, serves on for-profit and not-for-profit boards and is an industry professor at the University of South Australia.

WANT THE LATEST FROM QUARTERLY ESSAY?

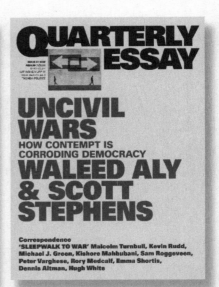

**Subscribe to the Friends of Quarterly Essay
email newsletter to share in news, updates,
events and special offers.**

---

quarterlyessay.com.au/signup

QUARTERLY ESSAY
BACK ISSUES

BACK ISSUES: (Prices include GST, postage and handling within Australia.) *Grey indicates out of stock.*

- ☐ **QE 1** ($22.99) Robert Manne *In Denial*
- ☐ **QE 2** ($22.99) John Birmingham *Appeasing Jakarta*
- ☐ **QE 3** ($22.99) Guy Rundle *The Opportunist*
- ☐ **QE 4** ($22.99) Don Watson *Rabbit Syndrome*
- ☐ **QE 5** ($22.99) Mungo MacCallum *Girt By Sea*
- ☐ **QE 6** ($22.99) John Button *Beyond Belief*
- ☐ **QE 7** ($22.99) John Martinkus *Paradise Betrayed*
- ☐ **QE 8** ($22.99) Amanda Lohrey *Groundswell*
- ☐ **QE 9** ($22.99) Tim Flannery *Beautiful Lies*
- ☐ **QE 10** ($22.99) Gideon Haigh *Bad Company*
- ☐ **QE 11** ($22.99) Germaine Greer *Whitefella Jump Up*
- ☐ **QE 12** ($22.99) David Malouf *Made in England*
- ☐ **QE 13** ($22.99) Robert Manne with David Corlett *Sending Them Home*
- ☐ **QE 14** ($22.99) Paul McGeough *Mission Impossible*
- ☐ **QE 15** ($22.99) Margaret Simons *Latham's World*
- ☐ **QE 16** ($22.99) Raimond Gaita *Breach of Trust*
- ☐ **QE 17** ($22.99) John Hirst *'Kangaroo Court'*
- ☐ **QE 18** ($22.99) Gail Bell *The Worried Well*
- ☐ **QE 19** ($22.99) Judith Brett *Relaxed & Comfortable*
- ☐ **QE 20** ($22.99) John Birmingham *A Time for War*
- ☐ **QE 21** ($22.99) Clive Hamilton *What's Left?*
- ☐ **QE 22** ($22.99) Amanda Lohrey *Voting for Jesus*
- ☐ **QE 23** ($22.99) Inga Clendinnen *The History Question*
- ☐ **QE 24** ($22.99) Robyn Davidson *No Fixed Address*
- ☐ **QE 25** ($22.99) Peter Hartcher *Bipolar Nation*
- ☐ **QE 26** ($22.99) David Marr *His Master's Voice*
- ☐ **QE 27** ($22.99) Ian Lowe *Reaction Time*
- ☐ **QE 28** ($22.99) Judith Brett *Exit Right*
- ☐ **QE 29** ($22.99) Anne Manne *Love & Money*
- ☐ **QE 30** ($22.99) Paul Toohey *Last Drinks*
- ☐ **QE 31** ($22.99) Tim Flannery *Now or Never*
- ☐ **QE 32** ($22.99) Kate Jennings *American Revolution*
- ☐ **QE 33** ($22.99) Guy Pearse *Quarry Vision*
- ☐ **QE 34** ($22.99) Annabel Crabb *Stop at Nothing*
- ☐ **QE 35** ($22.99) Noel Pearson *Radical Hope*
- ☐ **QE 36** ($22.99) Mungo MacCallum *Australian Story*
- ☐ **QE 37** ($22.99) Waleed Aly *What's Right?*
- ☐ **QE 38** ($22.99) David Marr *Power Trip*
- ☐ **QE 39** ($22.99) Hugh White *Power Shift*
- ☐ **QE 40** ($22.99) George Megalogenis *Trivial Pursuit*
- ☐ **QE 41** ($22.99) David Malouf *The Happy Life*
- ☐ **QE 42** ($22.99) Judith Brett *Fair Share*
- ☐ **QE 43** ($22.99) Robert Manne *Bad News*
- ☐ **QE 44** ($22.99) Andrew Charlton *Man-Made World*
- ☐ **QE 45** ($22.99) Anna Krien *Us and Them*
- ☐ **QE 46** ($22.99) Laura Tingle *Great Expectations*
- ☐ **QE 47** ($22.99) David Marr *Political Animal*
- ☐ **QE 48** ($22.99) Tim Flannery *After the Future*
- ☐ **QE 49** ($22.99) Mark Latham *Not Dead Yet*
- ☐ **QE 50** ($22.99) Anna Goldsworthy *Unfinished Business*
- ☐ **QE 51** ($22.99) David Marr *The Prince*
- ☐ **QE 52** ($22.99) Linda Jaivin *Found in Translation*
- ☐ **QE 53** ($22.99) Paul Toohey *That Sinking Feeling*
- ☐ **QE 54** ($22.99) Andrew Charlton *Dragon's Tail*
- ☐ **QE 55** ($22.99) Noel Pearson *A Rightful Place*
- ☐ **QE 56** ($22.99) Guy Rundle *Clivosaurus*
- ☐ **QE 57** ($22.99) Karen Hitchcock *Dear Life*
- ☐ **QE 58** ($22.99) David Kilcullen *Blood Year*
- ☐ **QE 59** ($22.99) David Marr *Faction Man*
- ☐ **QE 60** ($22.99) Laura Tingle *Political Amnesia*
- ☐ **QE 61** ($22.99) George Megalogenis *Balancing Act*
- ☐ **QE 62** ($22.99) James Brown *Firing Line*
- ☐ **QE 63** ($22.99) Don Watson *Enemy Within*
- ☐ **QE 64** ($22.99) Stan Grant *The Australian Dream*
- ☐ **QE 65** ($22.99) David Marr *The White Queen*
- ☐ **QE 66** ($22.99) Anna Krien *The Long Goodbye*
- ☐ **QE 67** ($22.99) Benjamin Law *Moral Panic 101*
- ☐ **QE 68** ($22.99) Hugh White *Without America*
- ☐ **QE 69** ($22.99) Mark McKenna *Moment of Truth*
- ☐ **QE 70** ($22.99) Richard Denniss *Dead Right*
- ☐ **QE 71** ($22.99) Laura Tingle *Follow the Leader*
- ☐ **QE 72** ($22.99) Sebastian Smee *Net Loss*
- ☐ **QE 73** ($22.99) Rebecca Huntley *Australia Fair*
- ☐ **QE 74** ($22.99) Erik Jensen *The Prosperity Gospel*
- ☐ **QE 75** ($22.99) Annabel Crabb *Men at Work*
- ☐ **QE 76** ($22.99) Peter Hartcher *Red Flag*
- ☐ **QE 77** ($22.99) Margaret Simons *Cry Me a River*
- ☐ **QE 78** ($22.99) Judith Brett *The Coal Curse*
- ☐ **QE 79** ($22.99) Katharine Murphy *The End of Certainty*
- ☐ **QE 80** ($22.99) Laura Tingle *The High Road*
- ☐ **QE 81** ($22.99) Alan Finkel *Getting to Zero*
- ☐ **QE 82** ($22.99) George Megalogenis *Exit Strategy*
- ☐ **QE 83** ($22.99) Lech Blaine *Top Blokes*
- ☐ **QE 84** ($22.99) Jess Hill *The Reckoning*
- ☐ **QE 85** ($22.99) Sarah Krasnostein *Not Waving, Drowning*
- ☐ **QE 86** ($27.99) Hugh White *Sleepwalk to War*
- ☐ **QE 87** ($27.99) Waleed Aly & Scott Stephens *Uncivil Wars*
- ☐ **QE 88** ($27.99) Katharine Murphy *Lone Wolf*

Please include this form with delivery and payment details overleaf.
Back issues also available as eBooks at **quarterlyessay.com**

SUBSCRIBE TO RECEIVE
10% OFF THE COVER PRICE

☐ **ONE-YEAR PRINT AND DIGITAL SUBSCRIPTION: $89.99**

- Print edition
- Home delivery
- Automatically renewing
- Full digital access to all past issues
- App for Android and iPhone users
- eBook files

DELIVERY AND PAYMENT DETAILS

DELIVERY DETAILS:

NAME:

ADDRESS:

EMAIL: PHONE:

PAYMENT DETAILS: Enclose a cheque/money order made out to Schwartz Books Pty Ltd.
Or debit my credit card (MasterCard, Visa and Amex accepted).
Freepost: Quarterly Essay, Reply Paid 90094, Collingwood VIC 3066
All prices include GST, postage and handling.

CARD NO. ☐☐☐☐ ☐☐☐☐ ☐☐☐☐ ☐☐☐☐

EXPIRY DATE: /   CCV: AMOUNT: $

PURCHASER'S NAME: SIGNATURE:

Subscribe online at **quarterlyessay.com/subscribe** • Freecall: 1800 077 514 • Phone: 03 9486 0288
Email: subscribe@quarterlyessay.com (please do not send electronic scans of this form)